Roberto Gonzalez is new in school, but he isn't going unnoticed. Janet is fascinated by this quiet, yet confident young man.

Tony is also aware of Roberto's presence, but not for the same reason. Janet is his girlfriend – or maybe she *was* his girlfriend.

Three is an odd number, an unacceptable number for Tony, and now it is time for him to even the score. But little does he suspect just who the mild-mannered Berto Gonzalez really is.

---

### *Even Odds*

Special Textbook-Edition featuring

•enhanced text for vocabulary building

•attractive illustrations

•end-of-book *Glossary*

**(128 pages)**

---

| | |
|---|---|
| *Computer Layout:* | *Toni Shortsleeve* |
| *Illustrated by:* | *Karen Petras* |
| *Cover Design:* | *Doug Behrens* |

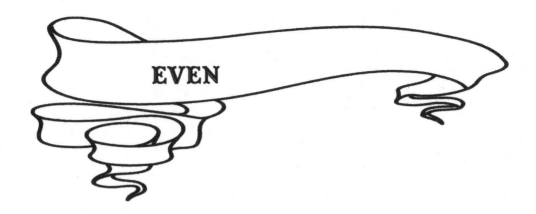

EVEN

Reading and building key vocabulary is a pleasurable experience when the stories are exciting and the text is challenging.

The enclosed tale is set in the Hawaiian Islands, but the adventures and lessons learned are universal.

Come let the Huckleberry Finn in you escape on a raft of unbounded fantasy and imagination as you embark on a verbally enriching odyssey with characters who will endear themselves to you through their personal and poignant escapades.

Let the journey begin...

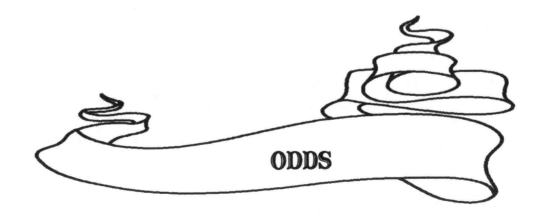

ODDS

# TABLE OF CONTENTS

# CHAPTER I
## *Coming To Town*

I don't know why I came to Hawaii. If it were up to me, I'd have stayed in cloudy Owry County with all my friends, soaking up the damp, cold air and the action that fit perfectly with it. Being here a month has been like living in paradise – boring and pointless. I don't mean to put it down but let's face it, it's a drag being here, away from the real world.

The people in my school are all loners. I mean they sit in small groups in all the classes, and they never seem to talk with people in other groups. Maybe it's just my imagination, but I tell you this place sucks.

The first day we arrived in Honolulu International Airport and stepped off the plane, me, my mom and my younger brother got our first taste of Hawaiian living – a jolt of Hawaiian humidity. It was as if we'd stepped into an oven, and even Jake was slowed down by the intense heat. Fact is, we hadn't ever before experienced such a warm day like this; the sun never shines in Owry County.

Don't get me wrong, though. Our first week in Hawaii wasn't all that bad. We stayed in a breezy Waikiki low-rise apartment, and Jake and I spent the whole day on the beach getting a golden-brown tan and meeting lots of **gregarious** tourists. For sure, the first week was the most exciting, but then it all got dull and routine. The sun hit us every day, the beaches got hotter by the hour, it seemed, and even the video arcades got **monotonous** after a while. I actually began to look forward to school, which was then only three weeks away.

I really don't know why we left Owry County. I think it happened because of "**irreconcilable** differences." Anyway, that's what my mom called it. Just a bunch of **petty** arguments that seemed to get worse as time went on. One thing led to another and suddenly, when I was in the middle of a softball game, Jake ran to tell me that we were going away. At first I thought he was joking, but then I feared far more than what had actually happened. I thought that maybe we were being thrown out.

Growing up in a place like Owry County isn't easy. It's not paradise; it's a jungle. Living my whole life there, I learned how to survive under any condition. Gangs, knives, drugs – they were the menu of the day, everyday. And the only good time of the day was waking up. After that it all went downhill. Just making it through the afternoon without getting into a fight was a miracle, and for those who were **crafty** enough to avoid fights – or win them all the time – there were more than enough chances to also get messed up with drugs. Pot, coke, ice, crack, it was all there, everyday. And I learned that the best way to survive was to join a gang and follow the leader.

I learned my share in Owry, but I'm rather glad that Jake isn't going to go through what I **endured**. I've still got the needle marks to prove what I did, and I know I'm gonna one day get busted in school for carrying around my *Benson & Hedges*. But there are certain things I'm still hooked on, and cigarettes is one of them.

It seems strange that I'm writing down the past month's events now that school has started, but the place is so boring that I find myself writing during lunch break just to make time go by faster. It's not that bad, but a part of me still **yearns** to be with Jerry and Sam and T.C. in Owry, **contriving** to **pilfer** from *Mr. M's Market* after school. I miss the action, but then again I spent two weeks in a **juvenile** center after we got caught one afternoon, so it wasn't really something I'd want to go through again. And I don't think my mom would, either.

When Jake told me we were "going away," I thought mom and dad had given up on us. I could understand them wanting to dump me, but not Jake. He was only eight years old then, and I'd distanced him from my **ignominious escapades** the best I could.

Jake and I became **cognizant** of the whole story when we got home. My dad had lost his job a week earlier, and the pressures were building between my mom and him. Apparently, tempers exploded during the day. I don't know for sure who got the worst of it, but I can guess. When we got home, my dad wasn't there, and we never saw him again.

We left two days later, headed straight for Honolulu, where my mom had some relatives. I liked the idea, but Jake cried all night. He kept saying, "I want to be with Roberto's friends," and at that precise moment I realized moving away was the best thing that could happen to him.

Now I really don't know. We're going to different schools, and I guess Jake has established a new **fraternity** of fellow **fledglings**. He seems to have found **fellowship** with his young **confreres** and is beginning to learn how to skateboard with them. But we're drifting apart, perhaps because I no longer **consort** with the **eclectic array** of **errant ne'er-do-wells** and therefore Jake doesn't have any reason to want to follow me around anymore. I think we did everything on the island that we could do together during the first couple of weeks, and now that school's started Jake's growing up on his own. Maybe it's the best for him, but I sure feel real lonely.

*...now that school's started, Jake's growing up on his own. Maybe it's the best for him, but I sure feel real lonely.*

## CHAPTER II
### *New Kid In School*

He's kind of cute. Just sits there by himself, **reclusive** and shy. I don't know why I like him. Could be he's the kind of boy that wants someone to be his friend. But how do I break the ice? My girlfriends would razz me to death if they thought I was trying to make the first move.

I heard his name's Roberto Gonzalez, but he looks more like he could be a singer for *The New Kids*. His mom must be part Spanish because he has long, soft lashes and a rounded, dimply face. His brownish-blond hair makes him look like a surfer, but I've heard he's only been in the islands for a few weeks.

I don't know why I'm always attracted to lonely-looking boys. Maybe it's the **maternal** instinct in me, or perhaps it's just that I find them to be less restrictive, less worried about their 'group image.' But if Tony were to know that I like Roberto, there would be trouble, guaranteed. I don't think Tony would take too well to having competition, and so I'll have to be careful and try secretly to become friends with Roberto. Having two boyfriends is cool, but not when one of them is Tony. For a ninth-grader, he's quite mature and not afraid to show someone else who's the real boss. Sometimes I wonder why I ever got to be his girlfriend, but I guess it happened because, two years ago, I saw him as the same type of lonely, **withdrawn** boy. Amazing how times can change a person. I miss the 'old' Tony. But I really like the new kid on the block.

I wonder what it's like to come to a new place – especially to an island like Hawaii, a land more culturally **diverse** than probably anywhere else in the world. Maybe I'll travel and live in the States one day, but since I've only visited the Mainland once I guess it'll be awhile before I can **savor** the **unconstrained** excitement of exploring new **habitats**.

Roberto doesn't seem to be very excited, though. He just sits alone during class and then spends his recess and lunchtime writing. Must be letters to all his friends back home. He's probably unhappy that he's had to leave everyone behind to come here. I wonder where he came from?

I heard he has a younger brother but his folks are separated. I know how that feels. My folks have threatened to break up for so many years. Sometimes I wish they'd just go through with it or stop the **idle** threats.

Tony's been my real **savior** from all my family problems. We spent enough evenings together when my parents were fighting, Tony rescuing me like a *Prince Charming* whenever I needed a **confidant**. He's really a nice boy, even though he's grown up too fast. In the seventh grade he was so peaceable and shy – just a lonely boy who wanted to have friends. And we became true friends, secret partners and one another's escape. His parents never put any restrictions on him, except that he would get locked out if he wasn't home by eleven. Then he'd have to sleep on the stairs or under the house.

*He's kind of cute. Just sits there by himself, reclusive and shy.*

I'll never forget the first time I saw his little nesting place, a little hideaway like a treehouse, but underneath the back-porch steps. I don't think his parents have ever noticed the small, **cordoned** area; if they did, Tony never mentioned it. When he showed it to me last year, it was during one of those **adversarial** evenings when my dad was drinking and my mom was itching to **instigate** a verbally **vitriolic engagement** for **domestic domination.**

I could sense the **venomous virulence seething** as I got home. My mom started yelling at me to wash the dishes, then she started telling me how my dad is just a drunken bum. When he got home, I knew he'd been drinking. The **slurred** speech, the wrinkled shirt, his unbuckled pants; it was all too **intoxicatingly** obvious. And my mom let him have it, right then and there – as though she herself had never ever touched the stuff. But I've seen her hide her Vodka bottles away, and I know she's got bottles in places I've never seen before. It's just like parents to try to act like they know what they're doing, masking all the while the very fact that they're more confused than us kids. It's just too bad they've forgotten how to communicate with one another. They'd rather fight – it's so much more 'grown-up.'

I called Tony at eight, and he invited me to come over. It's nice to live close to a friend like Tony. But not too close. A five-minute **commute** by bus, just close enough to get there without having to wait for a ride from my parents, but yet not so close in **proximity** that we'd soon become a pain in each other's side.

When I got to his house, it was already **pitch-dark.** The **lambent** moon was hidden behind the cloud-filled Hawaiian evening sky, and I felt a sense of security as we initially embraced. He then showed me the secret back-porch storage, which he called *steal away*, like the line in the song that goes "Why don't we steal away into the night." The room was so **plushly** decorated, like a real bedroom. He had used some concrete to make the floor solid, then **draped** a **shag** rug over it and even managed to construct wooden walls on all sides with a walkway through the front. The room was only five feet high, but it looked like it was built by a professional. It was then that I discovered just how little I really knew about Tony. All his quiet, shy ways masked his artistic, **resourcefully inventive** true inner self.

We spent the whole evening together, under the house and in dim candlelight. We **fabricated** our own mattress out of a sleeping bag and some pillows that he'd sneaked in from the house, and for the first time ever I felt as though I had some control over my life, as though I had a place to turn to if my own parents couldn't maintain peace between themselves. Tony and I were alone, each of us the only child in our families, but together that evening we shared an **inviolable** trust that made us brother and sister, friends for life, and maybe even more.

As the weeks passed, Tony and I made *steal away* look like an **aureate** palace. We lovingly **embellished** our personal **domicile** by inserting a small window and even adding a sofa to enhance those precious moments shared in our **intimate tête-à-tête.** But in the midst of our building and decorating, our **chimerical Elysian** romance began to fade, little by little. *Steal away* eventually became boring, my **affinity** for the hideaway **haven** replaced by detached disinterest and then **agitated aversion** altogether. Though Tony never suspected anything, things changed over the two years since we first met; we'd both grown physically and mentally. Our interests changed too, all except one: Tony still liked girls and I still liked boys. But the problem was, he still liked the same girl, whereas I was no longer so eager to spend the rest of my life with the same person. Not yet, anyway.

Roberto is so cute, so distant, so **enchanting**. But how do I ever expect to get to know him better? I know, I know. All my friends have already told me: "If you like something, go for it." But making friends is not like going shopping. You just can't rush in and grab what you want. And not someone like Roberto. The best prizes are the hardest to catch. But I only wish I knew how to **befriend** him without hurting Tony's pride or sparking a firestorm between the two. I know I'm walking a tightrope and that I'd better step carefully, especially around Tony. After all, he's not the same boy he was two years ago. He's now a gang leader.

# CHAPTER III
## *Going Down*

All day long, it's getting to be the same old story. Sitting here, staring at *Pac Man* and *Tron*, *Super Sprint* and *Double Dragon*. It's like an old re-run of a lousy movie. Why did the school have to allow these games on campus? I thought I'd had enough of them in Waikiki, but now they're here to haunt me during schooldays, too.

I've been messing up in school, making the worst kinds of friends, and even Janet seems to be losing interest in me. I just don't know what's been happening. Maybe I'm smoking too much and it's scrambling my brains. Or maybe I'm just the perfect kid to get into trouble. My folks haven't been coming down on me, so I don't know why I'm having so many problems.

I can see Janet looking at that new kid, the one with the new *Nikes*, the guy who acts so quiet, so innocent, such a wimp. I'd like to just catch him one day and crack him, just to show him who's the boss. But damn it, that's just like me. Always trying to make things worse instead of better. Like when I play *Double Dragon*, I'm the guy with the bat trying to beat up everyone else. It sounds real good in stories or with a video game, but when it's for real it's really a bummer.

I cracked Jeff last summer, right over the head with a baseball bat. Just cranked up and gave him a hit while he wasn't looking. Three weeks in the hospital. Twenty-eight stitches. And why? Just because he looked at Janet. Or maybe because I needed to blow off some steam, and Jeff was the only one I knew I could take on. Sure, with a bat. Big deal.

I became leader of the Dark Demons after that happened. George and Alex and Barry followed me like I was their chief, like I was special because I could waste someone. And they said I did it "without conscience," like it was something to be proud of. Like I was *Superman*. Yeah, like a stupid superman, like a real-life *Rambo*. Lots of guts but no brains.

"Give me a reason and I'll do anything," I used to say. So I started ripping off car antennas – for a 'reason.' Beating up young kids so I could take their money – for a 'reason.' And my friends convinced me it was for a real good reason too: because I have "no conscience." And when I started to believe them, they began to control me.

So, where am I now? Janet's looking the other way, my friends are getting more daring and want me to keep leading the way, and now I'm hooked on cigarettes, video, and who knows what else. Great combination.

Last night I slept in *steal away*, and I thought about everything that's happened in the past year, since the time the Dark Demons took over my life. With all the things I've done, I really wonder why I'm still in school. My folks care, but I don't seem to anymore. All I do is screw things up. My folks treat me with respect, but then I mess up everything with my own brand of twisted logic.

I remember last Christmas when we all went to Disneyland. My dad said it was the best present he could get me. And I remember how long I'd wanted to go there, with Mickey Mouse and all the fantasy rides. It was like a dream come true, but when I got there it wasn't like I'd planned. I think my dreams changed. I looked at the riverboat and tried to figure out ways to carve my initials in its side. The bumper cars were just plain boring, so I tried to make someone fall off so I could run him over. It wasn't fun – it was like an obsession, looking for trouble.

I finally got my kicks in the bathroom, where I **pummeled** another boy who entered after me. I just said something to him, he asked "What?" and then I landed a solid right and decked him. Then I spit on him and kicked him as I passed by to go out.

I guess I'm a really big man, huh? Sure, I can feel it when I walk around school. The other guys keep away from me; they don't even try to start anything. But I think I know the real reason why they avoid me. I thought I was tougher than everyone else, but last week John Christianson **sobered** me up. He's a monster. Two hundred pounds of muscle; nobody messes with him. He told me straight – "people think you're a bit wacky." All except my gang. I guess they're a bit wacky, too.

I'm not proud. I was proud when I hung around Janet and we shared peaceful moments together at *steal away*, the radio on low, Janet and me whispering to one another while ***Whitney Houston*** sang softly for us. And it wasn't that long ago. But I just got restless, that's all. And I'm still restless. I sit here and just think out loud, staring at those stupid video games. I've got my name scribbled all over them. Big deal. But I'm losing my girlfriend and don't even know what I'm doing anymore, and that's what really worries me.

Boy, I wish I could beat that new kid up. Just to even things. Make him feel scared and not know what's happening. Him and his stupid innocence in class and under that tree during lunch – so quiet and happy. And I can see Janet looking at him. She likes him. Just like she once liked me.

Damn it, why am I losing my grip? I can feel myself getting more and more screwed up every day. Maybe a few smokes will help. But it's never helped in the past. I want to get that boy. I want to get him real bad.

*I wish I could beat that new kid up. Just to even things.*

# CHAPTER IV
## *A New World*

Time is really flying by. I haven't made many friends yet, but I'm beginning to talk to more people, especially girls. They're not like the girls in Owry County. Maybe it's because we're all a bit older, so it's easier to chat with them. Or maybe I'm just a stranger and they're fascinated by me.

Carla asked me why I'm always writing, and I told her it's because I used to watch the *Waltons* and idolized Jon-boy. She laughed, but I think she likes me a lot. She's so pretty and she's quiet, too. Maybe that's just the way everybody is here – quiet but nice. It's not like Owry. There, the only way to survive is to be faster or more street-smart than everyone else. I was a bit of both. Fast enough to **evade** the cops, wiry enough to hop the fences and slide between cars, and gutsy enough to know when and how to fight.

You don't need to be strong in Owry County. In fact, strength means nothing. I remember a guy who got in a fight in Santa Rivera Junior High. He took off his shirt and flexed his triceps in **doughty defiance**. The other guy smiled, pulled out a **stiletto** and carved his name all over the stud. It was a bloody joke. Nobody messes around in Owry unless they've got more than their fists.

Here at Ocean View School, I've been able to just sit back, cruise and catch up with my life. Even Jake has stayed out of trouble. It's been like a vacation – boring but safe. I'm even getting to like it here, too. I'm not so uptight and I'm getting a thrill out of writing everything down. I might even ask Carla to go to the next school dance when it comes up.

There's another side to the story, however. Although I've **forged** an **equanimity** with my inner self, I know I'm not fitting in too well with the other guys. I can feel it when I walk into class. They look at me with **disdainful antipathy**, **piqued** because I have made no effort to enlist in their **fold** of **frittering** fools. They **glower** at me as though they think I'm afraid, that I'll start crying one day. But I simply smile casually and turn away. I know better than to look at anyone too long. I'm not looking for trouble, and I'll steer clear from it as long as I can. However, I don't suspect that anyone seriously wants to **provoke** me. In fact, the environment here **exudes** a **tranquillity** the likes of which I have never before experienced. Rather than awake to a **bellicose** world of **coercion** and **intimidation**, I can let my guard down and do what I really feel like doing. It's a pretty good scene. Even the teachers are cool.

I never thought I'd spend my lunchtime writing. Back in Owry, people don't write; they fight. It's really hard to become somebody when all you've got to look forward to is who you'll be rubbing the wrong way next or who you'll meet that you know you can beat up. There's no time to yourself, no chance to just kick back and **contemplate** why things are the way they are. I know I'm no writer but I feel that what I'm saying is so real for me, and maybe for others my age. I want to write, I really want to show the world that I am somebody who has something to say. And I don't want to show it by putting a bomb underneath the auditorium chairs. That doesn't say anything. It only makes things worse for everyone.

I can't remember anything I did last year that was really worth writing about, except perhaps when I beat up Jake. But that happened as a result of a **conjunction** of **conspiring** circumstances.

Jake's nine years old now and he's going through a **narcissistic** age in which he thinks he's the best person in the world. He doesn't care about anyone else. Everything's got to be for him. But I know he still looks up to and **reveres** me, even though he doesn't need my help like he did in Owry. There, we had to support each other just to survive. I remember when a pack of sixth-graders cornered him in the hall. I picked up a garbage can and just stood there, like *Clint Eastwood*, quiet and determined, and they all knew I'd have flattened them with it if they didn't cease and **desist** at that very moment. They scattered as quickly as though I'd set them on fire, Jake just standing there crying – **coweringly** thanking me in between sobs. But he returned the favor before the school year was up. And it happened under very awkward conditions, right after I'd left the City Slickers and joined the **rival** Downtown Damned.

Friends can change almost overnight. I've never placed too much trust in them. They're **fickle** and will support you only as long as you support them, but once the pressure's on they'll leave you at the drop of a hat. I only respect those few people who'll stand by you when they've got nothing to gain from it. I had no such friends in the City Slickers. That's why I left.

Skip Sugarello was my reason for joining the Damned. It all started on Saturday, midway through the second half of the eighth-grade school year, and it climaxed with the help of my little brother.

I don't know what it's like to be **destitute**, hungry and neglected. I admit that my folks were never the best role models for me, but at least we've always had food on the table. And I've tried my best to watch over Jake; he's always had an older brother to lean on and look up to. But I never had anyone to follow or pattern myself after. So I drifted, joining the Slickers for three months before I realized that ripping off department stores and ganging up on little kids wasn't my kind of fun. All my actions pointed toward an **irretrievable retrogression** headed for total self-**annihilation**, and being busted twice in the same week didn't **bode** well for any miraculous reversal of fortune. Then I teamed up with Skip, a model student and star basketball player **lionized** by the community for his **civility** and **sophistication**. In short, he didn't seem to belong in Owry. Little did I suspect that he possessed more than met the eye. My first impression was that he was the smoothest talker I'd ever met. He could charm a person into giving him anything, and his **prepossessing** personality and **self-deprecating mien** really made you feel good doing it. Even in the cloudiness of the County, Skip always had something **festive** or **uplifting** to say, though he never sounded **supercilious** or **ostensibly patronizing**. He was everybody's friend, a rare sight in an environment where having friends really seemed out of place.

I can't figure out if Skip really had any **bosom** buddies, because he never pushed himself on others. He'd just smile and keep to himself. The girls would practically **swoon** when the **charismatic** *Adonis* spoke to them in his soft, **mellifluous** voice, but he never gave them a chance to get too close. He was always on the go, studying for exams or going to a basketball game. He had no time for casual conversation, nothing more than a **cordial** "hello" and a courteous "goodbye."

But Skip really showed his true colors when I got in a squeeze. The Slickers were **vexed** and **nettled** when I informed them I was quitting the club, and they made clear their threats to me. I anticipated the after-school **confrontation**, and I knew it was a fate I'd have to accept: let them beat me up and then they'd leave me alone.

I bumped into them that afternoon, right outside math class. I was with Jake when four of the Slickers came up to me. They told Jake to get lost, threatening to beat him up if he didn't leave. Jake ran, and I honestly felt then that my kid brother was the biggest coward I'd ever known.

Matt Spark had the first words. "You're leaving us, huh 'Shiloh'?"

I answered back **apprehensively**. I liked my nickname, a name they'd given to me, but I also knew they weren't my friends. And as I wasn't about to **cringe** in **unctuous servility** and plead for **absolution**, so too did I know they'd leave their mark on me before the afternoon was through.

I was escorted to one of our club hangouts, the group **flanked** in typical mob fashion. The few words they spoke attacked my allegiance, my personality and my manliness. They enjoyed the session of humiliation, and I let them pursue their **perverse** pleasures without **remonstration**.

We turned down Mercer Avenue toward one of the **ramshackle** houses that the Slickers proudly called 'home,' when suddenly out of nowhere a group of **rival** members appeared. They were awesome: dressed in studs, black jeans and black t-shirts, faces covered with ski masks. There must have been ten or twelve guys, all of them our age or older. They just stood **dauntlessly** in front of us, clubs in hand and prepared for **sanguinary** slaughter.

The Slickers stopped in their tracks, **petrified**. I too was scared; this wasn't anything I'd ever **encountered** before. They looked like professionals, like a **fearsome** young 'hit squad' that had invaded Owry.

"What do you want with us?" Matt asked, his face **ashen** and his words weak.

No response.

"Whatever you want, you can have it." Matt was **turning yellow**. It was written all over the **craven** leader.

The most **intimidating** of the **juvenile juggernaut** stepped forward. "We want Shiloh, and we want him now." His voice was rough, low and threatening. He wasn't kidding.

I was almost instantly abandoned, my execution squad turning and fleeing down the street in the direction of the school. No one in the group wanted to stick around. I stood alone

"Well, well, well, you are pretty brave, huh?" the leader chuckled.

"So what?" I replied with **indignation**. I didn't like being made into a spectacle. I was ready for a duel, one-sided though it would surely be.

"Join with us, **comrade**." The request was **proffered** in **earnest**, and I stood momentarily **dumbfounded**, **pondering** the invitation. Then I noticed a small, maskless boy in the middle of the group. "Jake!" I cried, afraid that he was being kidnapped.

"I told you I'd help, Berto," he answered **gleefully**, coming out from within the circle and approaching me quickly, hugging me as we met. The **august entourage** removed their disguise, and we became officially introduced.

I did join the Damned, and I discovered just why Skip was everybody's 'friend.' He possessed a magnetism that attracted followers, and for those who weren't conned by his sweet words he had enough power to make them **grovel** to his every command. He was the leader of the newest, most powerful group in Owry: the Downtown Damned.

Jake was lucky that he'd chanced upon Skip that afternoon, and I was grateful to both of them. Jake was not the **apostate** I had initially mislabeled him as, and Skip turned out to be a most welcome **formidable ally**. But the power and the glory soon got to Jake's head. It was just a matter of time before I had to **disabuse** him and let him know where he was really headed.

Jake's not a bad little brother. In fact, he's a bit of a wimp. He's the kind of boy who picks on kids half his size but cries if he's up against an even match. He fit perfectly into the lifestyle of Owry, where the bullies rule. And having become friends with Skip, Jake began to think he was now someone special, someone who could get away with anything because he happened to know the 'right person.'

At first I didn't mind him **wielding** his new-found authority and **browbeating** the other kids. I let him hang around the halls **harassing** and **cowing** the younger boys; I even walked by without commenting when I saw him smoking during the morning recess. I had no reason to try to stop him from acting **macho**. After all, it sure beat behaving like a wimp. Even the older kids left him alone when they found out he was Skip's friend.

But Jake was just kidding himself. He was never really Skip's friend. Skip knew who I was and knew he had the chance to secure my services. Jake simply offered him that **opportune** chance to get close to me, that's all. And I knew it. But why spoil his fun? After all, when you're Jake's age you need to have an older friend. Life's too lonely for a kid without friends.

*"I told you I'd help, Berto,"* he answered gleefully, coming out from within the circle...

Jake pushed it too far one day, and it was with Sandy Connors, the **timorous** and **diminutive** five-year-old freckle-faced redhead who lived next door to us. I came home from school on Friday and heard Sandy screaming hysterically. He lay **prostrate** in the driveway between our two houses, Jake on top of him, slapping him mercilessly across the face.

I dropped my books when I saw what was happening and pounced on Jake.

"Hey, what do you think you're doing?" I yelled as I yanked him off Sandy. Jake pulled away and flashed a pocket knife at me, shouting obscenities, adding "I'm the boss."

"The boss of what?" I demanded impatiently.

"Of everything," he answered back. "I'm the best, and if you don't think so, you'll become just like Sandy."

I looked at my **bedraggled** young neighbor and saw a knife-cut extending two inches across his left cheek, blood still oozing from it. I couldn't believe what I was looking at.

"It's my initial, Berto," Jake **proclaimed exultantly**. "He's gonna wear that 'J' across his face forever. Now he knows who's the boss."

At that moment, my mind went blank. All I can remember was charging my little brother, throwing him against the wall and punching him everywhere, as many times as I could. I felt no pain, no conscience, no hesitation. I simply did what I had to, and I don't know whether I blacked out from exhaustion or from the knife cut in my belly.

Jake survived. He was beaten up pretty bad, but nothing was broken. And I survived – I always have and always will. Twelve stitches closed up the knife wound, and I was back in school on Monday. I never even felt the knife penetrate my body as I lunged towards Jake. I don't think he actually meant to stab me; I think I just landed on the knife during my surprise attack.

And Sandy survived. The wound was generally **superficial**, and his parents didn't do more than simply threaten **litigation** if it happened again. My folks were also pretty cool about it. Actually, I think they were more worried about my cut than about Sandy's parents, and I never heard about the incident again from anyone. Not from my parents, not Sandy's. And Jake and I didn't ever talk about it again. That happened seven months before we moved, but it stopped Jake from getting into any further trouble. My last few months weren't quite so **placid**.

# CHAPTER V
## *Mixed Feelings*

Tony's becoming a real drag, an **insufferable megalomaniac**. He told me last week that I should hang around him more. But the more I see him, the more I notice how much he's changed. He's grown his hair longer, he's even beginning to sport a tiny mustache. And his voice is so far away, so uncommunicative. I should feel sorry for him, but *he* doesn't even care about himself anymore. He merely hangs around his **philistine** friends **engineering infantile atrocities** to **pander** to his **hooligans' hedonistic predilections** and **satiate** his own **quixotic lust** for **omnipotence**. *Steal away* hasn't been cleaned for months, and when I dropped by last week it no longer **radiated** the **blithe** and **vernal vivacity redolent** of happier days. When we were building it up, I knew already that I was losing that feeling of romance and excitement the secret hideaway once held. But now it doesn't even look like it did before; there's not a single reminder left of those golden moments we used to share.

I haven't got anything against Tony. He's still my boyfriend. He'll always be my friend, but maybe not like before. Perhaps *I've* changed. Perhaps I've begun to demand too much from him. It was fun when we were playing 'pretend,' but once our house became too real the fantasy disappeared. Maybe that's what happened, but I really think Tony's changed, too. He's lost that spark of magic, that desire to create. He's become content living the life of gang leader, of **malcontent**. He's not really even a leader anymore, no longer that mischievous pioneer I once loved. Now he's just a **pompous egotist motivated** by **grandiose delusions** of superiority.

When did Tony change? And why did he change? I wish I knew for sure. I wish there was something I could do or say to bring back the Tony I once knew, but I guess he's happy being who he is, and that's why we're drifting apart. I'm not happy with who he is, but there's really nothing I can do to change him back.

I've really been fascinated by Berto. Gee, I feel stupid writing in my diary about Tony and then shifting my thoughts to Berto. But he's really been my inspiration this school year. We haven't spoken very many times, but every time we do I fall more in love with him. He's so warmhearted and **endearingly** sensitive and always talks about his younger brother to me. I think that Jackie is the only person he has who really needs him, and I feel so close to both of them when I listen to Berto. If only Tony had a little brother like Jackie, maybe he'd have more reason to **eschew** his Demon **cohorts**. But then again, if they were brothers he'd probably make Jackie join his **unsavory** band of **intractable delinquents**.

I keep returning to Tony in my thoughts. I wonder if my attraction to Berto is on the rebound – as a result of my falling out with Tony. Or is it sincere? Do I really love him, or is it a misplaced **vicarious** love that I really have for Tony?

Tony stopped me last week.  He got mad at me for talking about Berto and he slapped me.  No real reason; maybe jealousy, perhaps.  He gave me a solid backhand across my face, and I stopped talking, looked him straight in the eye, turned and walked away.

My dad smacks me kind of often, especially when he comes home **inebriated** and I haven't managed to get out of his way.  But he doesn't do anything else to me.  He's not like some other fathers who say things that mess up a person's mind.  He just smacks me.  Like he thinks I'm my mom or something.  But then he walks away, **sulking**.  I just take it in **stride**.  I'm used to it.  I don't like it, but I don't fight it, either.

Nobody else besides Tony and my dad have ever slapped me.  I had a near fight last year, but it ended fast.  Wanda Berman got **saucy** because she thought I had ripped off her wallet.  I knew who really did it, but I was **mum** from the moment she accused me.

"Give it back," she threatened, "or else I'll beat you up."  The words were so **trite**, so **feckless**.

Comparatively, my reply was **akin** to an atomic bomb:  "Touch me, Wanda, and I'll stick my fingers through your eyes."

I never saw a person cool her temper so quickly.  She apologized right then and there, and nobody ever tried to test my words again.  And I'm glad they didn't.  I meant every word I'd said.

I really hate getting mad.  It's such a waste of time.  My friends spend so much time **bickering**, but I just avoid involving myself in any such **fracas** by telling them to do what they want.  I think most of them enjoy **squabbling**, which is their problem, not mine.  But then again, maybe I'm just like them, too.  After all, my boyfriend is a real problem.

If I were Berto's girlfriend, I wonder how things would be?  I sometimes **envision** myself strolling with him and Jackie to the park or going swimming with them on weekends.  I suddenly have my own family.  I really want to have a family.

In fact, I asked Tony last year if he'd like to become a daddy.  It sounded funny to him, but I meant it very seriously.  It's been a dream of mine since I first saw Tony.  When he looked **coyly** at me with his almond eyes – the dark brown pupils penetrating my soul – I knew I wanted to know him, share myself with him, and explore life with him.

I remember that day so well, when he turned around in math class and stared into my eyes, then looked suddenly away as though afraid he was intruding upon my personal space.  The meeting was accidental, but our eyes locked together for a brief eternity, and we were **intimately intertwined** from that moment on.

Here I go, **digressively rambling** about Tony again.  I don't know whether I'm still in love with him or whether I'm in love with the way he used to be.  How do married people survive so long together?  Is it because they still love one another or is it perhaps because they remember just how much they once loved each other?  And is that enough reason to still be together?  Should I continue to stand by Tony even if he's not the person he used to be?  I still love him, even with all his hangups.  But the simple fact is that we're not as close as we used to be.  We just don't share anything anymore.  Instead, he simply tells me what to do with no regard for my own personal feelings.  It's like we've become an old and **estranged** married couple.

What should I do?  Life is so confusing, sometimes.  I want to get to know Berto, but I still love Tony. *Dear Abby*, can you please help me?

# CHAPTER VI
## *The Slap*

I'm sorry I hit Janet. I think it just shows how screwed up I really am. It's been building up inside of me for a year or so, ever since I started to rule the Demons – ever since all the other boys started expecting me to be their leader. There's nothing special about being a leader. Being on top is the pits. You can't do anything without everyone else watching you, ready to follow you. It's like being a **sitcom** character on TV. You get a reputation and then you're forced to follow it, stupid though that may seem. I found that out fast. Everything I did seemed to be for the club, not for me. No matter what I did, my **minions** would talk about how I did it better than anyone else because I'm the Demon-leader. And I truly believed them, just like I guess everyone else does when they let themselves get carried away by what other people tell them.

I slapped Janet because she said something I didn't like. She told me to "grow up." I couldn't accept that. I wasn't ready for her honesty.

"I'm not your slave," I told her. I acted the part of Demon leader when I said it, imagining I was talking back to my folks. They would always listen, though I knew they could care less what I had to say. I'd get the words out of my system, and it wouldn't even matter to them; they'd just smile and let me **proclaim** my discontent. But it did matter to Janet, and she showed it.

"I don't care who you think you are. I *know* who you are. And you're not acting like the real you."

"So what," I snapped back hotly. "Who do you think *you* are? My mother?"

"No, I'm trying to be your friend." She was silent for a moment after that and then looked at me, right into my eyes. I turned away.

"You can't even look at me, straight in the face. Are you afraid or something?" She was testing me, not really expecting an answer.

I looked at her for an instant, but I felt the shame of truth: I really couldn't look at her. I felt **uneasy** and sort of foolish, perhaps because her honesty was so unlike the **saccharine servility** my **fawning** flock **foisted** upon me. She wasn't flattering me; she was being honest with me, like a true friend.

"So, what do you want from me?" I asked **sheepishly**, trying not to have to look at her. But she made me.

"I want to see you, Tony. I want to talk to you, not to the side of your head. And take off those silly sunglasses. They make you look like a **poseur**.

*"So, what do you want from me?"* I asked sheepishly...

I didn't like her reference to my glasses. They were a part of my personality, my **disposition**, my **status** as leader. I needed to defend myself. "Don't put me down..." I replied **contentiously**. I wanted to add another word to shut her up, but the word didn't come out. I was afraid of the consequences.

"Then get off your high horse, Tony. Get off while you still can." She paused, then added "Or maybe you can't."

I knew then we were about to **embark** upon a **portentous altercation**. I wanted to leave but I couldn't just walk away. "Leave me alone, okay?" I pleaded.

"No, I won't. I like you too much. I'm part of your problem."

"I didn't ask you to be," I shouted. "It's your decision."

"So what? You don't want me to be your friend?"

"I didn't say that." I was getting **flustered** and **befuddled**. I knew that Janet was testing me, trying to make me decide between my gang friends and her friendship. I chose to ignore her logic and pursued my own brand of common sense. "Look, my friends have always been beside me, and that's the way they want it. Nobody asked them to join me and they never asked me to lead them. It just happened that way, and that's how it is." The explanation made sense to me. It was simple and therefore logical.

But Janet demanded more than mere rehearsed **rhetoric**. "How is it, really, Tony?" she asked with daggers in her eyes.

"It's good, Janet, really good. And if I don't look at you, it's because I just don't think you'll ever understand it. You just don't understand where I'm at or where I'm coming from."

"Tony, I know where you're at. And I know who you are." Janet's voice was **stern** and filled with **rage**. "You're the boss of a bunch of **derelicts**, a group of failures who look up to you because you're the biggest failure of them all."

My pulse began to rush as she continued.

"And I'm a bigger fool than you to hang around you and accept your **paltry** excuses. Tony, you are a failure, and one day I'll be strong enough to realize it and get away from you and your do-nothing so-called friends."

Then she dropped the bomb on me.

"You should act more like Roberto Gonzalez, that new boy in school. At least he's got brains enough not to be told what to do."

Those last few words harpooned themselves into my **ego**, attacking every last **vestige** of pride I had for myself. She was destroying my front, exposing me as everything I was trying not to become. Not only was I losing face with Janet, but worse yet she had already chosen a replacement for me.

I rolled my hand into a fist, **yearning** for the other boy to be around so I could **vent** all my frustration into his stomach. But he wasn't there, and all I could do was defend myself **ineffectually** with words. "I'm not a failure." I wanted to say much more. I wanted to be *Mark Antony* as he **vigorously** and **dynamically** defended *Julius Caesar*. But I lacked his **eloquence**. Instead, all I could do was deny the truth and **delude** myself into believing that my character was **laudable** and deserving of **dignity**. We both knew that was a lie. I was surely no **champion** of **righteousness**. But still, how could my best friend call me a failure and compare me unfavorably with a boy she didn't even know? What did he have to offer that I didn't? Or had I changed so much that I no longer offered anything attractive to anyone else?

My confidence was shaken. I was no longer Number One in everyone's eyes. Janet wasn't supporting me anymore, and I couldn't even defend myself without looking more foolish. I was losing the very person who meant the most to me. I could sense that I was heading in a hopelessly wrong direction, with no clear way to turn around.

"So what should I do?" I asked Janet with **measured nonchalance** after a seemingly **interminable** pause.

"Whatever you want. I don't care." She turned to leave, but I had to hear more.

"No, don't tell me you don't care," I **implored**, holding her shoulder as she turned.

"Don't touch me anymore," she replied **brusquely**. " I don't ever want you to touch me again. Why don't you just grow up?"

The words were hard and bruising. I felt a semi-unconsciousness enveloping me. The finality of her response was totally unexpected. I stood **agape**, in shock. Then, as though my hand had a will of its own, I heard it slap across Janet's face, echoing as if rattling against a large window. I pulled the hand back, but it was too late. Janet started crying as she ran away from me – whether from the pain, surprise, or the frustrating **futility** of the situation, I really don't know. I called out to her, but she was gone.

Our brief conversation was over, yet I realized just how much had been said. It had revealed to me how far apart we had grown, and how **onerous** even a simple conversation had become. Janet had started off trying to communicate with me – trying to be my friend – but by the end of our **discourse** I had totally turned her off. Worse yet, my **artless articulation** and **otiose** attempts at **oratory** didn't even convince myself. My last gesture was truly the sign of a loser, a failure. I was the leader of a bunch of followers, and now I realized I was the biggest follower of them all. I took off my sunglasses and walked **dejectedly** towards the Demon's den, hopeful that I might **encounter** the **rival** who had replaced me.

# CHAPTER VII
## *The Skateboard*

There's a really nice girl in one of my classes, and I didn't even notice her until a couple of weeks ago, when she came up to me and introduced herself. She's cute and she's got a really mature personality. Compared to her, Carla and Veronica are mere **adolescent** schoolgirls. When she speaks to me, I become **enriched** with inspiringly **innovative** ideas, and I find myself wanting to write more and more after I see her. She fills my thoughts with **rapturous** delight and seems genuinely interested in learning more about Jake and me.

I'm looking forward to asking her to the high school prom that's coming up in a couple of months. It's not like in Owry, where girls are just objects to **bolster** the boys' *Superman* egos. Maybe it's different here because I'm a bit older and so are the people I hang around. But I think it's also because I don't belong to a punk group like the Damned.

I was really glad to get away from Skip's band of **malevolent** misfits. A month before we moved to Honolulu, three of us were caught while trying to **appropriate** another boy's skateboard. Jerry, Sam and I had planned it for a while, watching the proud but **naïve** kid skate by daily like clockwork with his eighty-dollar *Silvercloud* board. We had no trouble getting it from him, especially since he was three years younger than either of us. He also knew us and didn't want any trouble. It went smooth as silk.

"Hey Robbie, how's it going dude?" I asked casually as I approached from the other side of the street, **flanked** by my other gang members.

"Oh, hi Shiloh. How's everything?" His voice **resonated** in a **tremulous timbre** as he stood with one foot atop his board. He made no motion to pick it up, fearing that it would draw our attention. But we already knew why we were there. The rest was **predetermined**.

"Nice board you got there, dude. Mind if I ride it?" My **peremptory** remark was not meant to be answered, only approved. Robbie Turner had no choice. He looked hopelessly up at the sky, then stared at me blankly and replied, "Sure." No other word would have **befit** the occasion. He strolled the board over to us, one foot on the pavement and the other firmly planted on his prize possession.

In a flash I was on the board, riding triumphantly down the street while Jerry and Sam jogged along. We never looked back and Robbie didn't call out for us. He might have wanted to, but the words never reached our ears. The board was mine.

Twenty-four hours later, I was in the **juvenile** cell block with the other two guys. We had known Robbie for a year or so, when he first moved into the neighborhood, and considered him easy **prey**. We knew his dad, too, whom we informally called by his first name, "Sarge." But only after the incident did we discover that "Sarge" wasn't really his first name – it was short for "Sergeant," as in

"Police Sgt. Turner." Our **roguish escapade** had backfired right in our faces, and I felt the **brunt** of the **witless** act that landed me behind bars. I deserved every bit of it. I had no regrets about being there. Maybe I could learn from it.

Jake really helped me see where I was heading. He provided that shock I needed. When he and mom visited me there at the cell, he was proud of me. "Berto, I want to grow up to be as bad as you," he beamed with **emulating aspiration**.

Ashamed and humiliated, all I could do was sit on the bunk and turn away from him as he watched from the other side of the room. My mom **whisked** Jake away, slapping him on the side of his head as if to say "Don't hang around him; he's no good."

I knew at that very moment I needed to change my **ignoble** ways, make **amends** and chart a new course – or else see myself fall deeper and deeper into crime and self-destruction. I hungered for a cigarette, but I was alone, without my family, without anyone to lean on. I had fallen into an **abyss** of **abject desolation** and was witnessing firsthand what life was like for people who have nothing. I had tried to act like a big man and all I got for it was busted and rejected.

Jerry and Sam were in different holding tanks, and I was sure their folks would come to bail them out. But I wasn't so sure about my own. Mom made it pretty clear that she didn't **countenance** my actions, and Jake's comments didn't help **mitigate** the severity of the situation.

My hunch was right. I spent the weekend in the **infernal** facility, whereas Jerry and Sam were quickly **liberated**. Two days later the police released me, apparently because they couldn't hold me any longer without formal charges. Sgt. Turner gave me a break by not throwing the book at me, or at least I hoped he wasn't going to. All I wanted to do was get away from there, away from the **dank** cell and the **squalid** station and the whole cursed city. I couldn't find anything worth doing in the town anymore, nothing that would keep me out of trouble.

I really didn't mind leaving Owry County, even at the expense of my folks breaking up. I had more to lose by staying, so when mom gave me the choice of staying with dad or moving with her to Hawaii I jumped at the opportunity to leave my **sordid** past behind and start **anew**. I had nothing against dad – if indeed he planned on coming back – but I was tired of the Demons, tired of **perpetrating puerile ploys**, and tired of seeing myself as a **pathetic pariah**. Skip's group really offered no glamour, only bittersweet memories. The Damned kept me out of minor daily **squabbles** but then gave me a false sense of security which landed me in more serious trouble. The more secure I felt, the more idiotic I became. And **purloining** Turner's board without even knowing that his dad was the Sergeant was truly the height of ignorance.

**Ascending** the stairs to board the plane with Jake and mom, I left my shame and humiliation behind; and as I stepped into the corridor to enter the cabin, I felt as though a new beginning awaited me. I knew I would be a total stranger in a new land, but I also knew I wouldn't have **upstart**

**antagonists** or **zealous adherents adversely** affecting my decisions.  I was ready to begin from scratch and restructure my life – and Jake's, too.

I think things have gone pretty well; I've had a quiet three months so far.  As the Christmas holidays approach I feel as though mom, Jake and I can all be grateful for maintaining a **cohesive** family unit, one which has managed to **endure** the **trials** and **tribulations** of the past year.  And I've met some of the cutest girls without worrying about their jealous boyfriends or gang-leaders.  Honolulu truly is a unique place where one can rediscover oneself in undisturbed **serenity**.

# CHAPTER VIII
## *A Believer*

I haven't seen Tony for two weeks. I only **conversed** briefly with him once, the day after he slapped me, and now we don't even look at one another. He avoids me when we're in the same building. In history class he sits on the far side of the room. And I haven't made any move to **ameliorate** matters, either. I'm just not interested in returning to an unpleasant situation. It's like someone trying to **goad** you into smoking a cigarette after you've finally kicked the habit. I've finally been able to survive the evening without needing to hear Tony's voice, so there's no reason to tempt myself during the day.

I've also found myself getting closer with Berto. We went out for ice cream and even watched a movie together last weekend. He's a very **docile** and **unobtrusive** individual who **relishes** observing life as it unfolds in his newfound **utopia**. He doesn't let anything get him down or make him angry, and even though he told me he used to smoke he's never once lit up while I've been around him.

I wonder if Tony is jealous. He's seen me with Berto but I've never talked with him about it. I don't want to hurt Tony, but his personality and mine have become so **polarized** that there's no reason for me to even ask him anything anymore. He's one of the Demons, and as long as that's his ultimate ambition he can **trifle** with his **toadies** and **idle** away his life without me.

The Christmas prom is coming up in two weeks, and I'm looking forward to going with Berto. He even asked me if he could take his little brother along – this is obviously the first prom he's ever gone to! But he seems so confident underneath his **demure** exterior, as though he possesses a secret inner strength which he doesn't share with others. I caught a glimpse of this **subtle self-assurance** after the movie. It happened right outside the theater, where we were approached by a band of **ruffians** in Waikiki.

Roberto and I had gone out only two times before – once to *Ala Moana Shopping Center* and once to Makaha Beach. But although we enjoyed moments spent looking at clothes together, we really got to know each other better at the beach, where we **basked** in the sun and shared **confidential** thoughts about school and friends – and of course, about one another.

I discovered much about Berto on the beach at Makaha, and I guess I must have **imparted** to him all the **minuscule** details of my own **uneventful** life. But I hadn't yet discovered that deep masculine streak of his until last Friday at the movies. Before then I still figured him to be a quiet, **introspective** boy who spent most of his time alone, writing notes to himself and **savoring** the **solitude**.

Berto met me in Waikiki on Friday. We live a couple miles apart, and since neither of us has our own transportation the bus was our ticket around town and the bus stop our **rendezvous** point. Berto told me he used to skateboard in his old neighborhood but since coming to Hawaii had put his wheels away. I think the real reason he preferred taking the bus to skateboarding was so we could meet, almost in a **clandestine** way, and **perambulate** side-by-side towards our ultimate **Elysian** destination.

I really don't know if Roberto is rich, but he sure dressed with **panache** and **flair** that night. He wore his black-striped *Lacoste* pullover with white *Jimmy 'Z* trousers and brand new *Adidas* basketball shoes. His hair was reddish in the front; he'd obviously tinted it specially for the occasion.

What really gave him character were his *Oakley* shades and a *Primo* cap, making him look like an **eccentric** millionaire golfer who just happened to wind up in Waikiki rather than *Waialae*. I stood there **transfixed** in **euphoric elation** as he **alighted jauntily** from the bus, gazed at me from behind the glasses and smiled. Actually it was more like a grin, as though he were proud of his own appearance. But his words weren't so **flamboyant**.

"Hi Janet. Gee, you sure look swell."

I was thrilled to hear that he liked what he saw. I'd spent an hour just brushing my hair, and I wore my newest *Levi's* blue jeans – which **accentuated** my somewhat-attractive hips – matched with a white *Calvin Klein* blouse that hugged tightly against my body. Those few simple words from Roberto made it all worthwhile. Tony had stopped complimenting me a year ago, and I'd almost forgotten just how good it felt to be appreciated rather than be taken for granted. Roberto had instantly won my heart.

"Hi, Berto," I replied dreamily. "You look like a movie star."

"Nah, I'm just a school-kid trying to look like one." The **reserve** in his **unassuming** response made my heart warm up even more. He was so **ingenuous**, so **unpretentious**, so 'himself.' It was a wonderful change from the **swaggering braggarts** in school – especially Tony, the **epitome** of **braggadocio**.

Roberto and I held hands right from the beginning of the evening. It seemed so natural, although we had never touched each other before. In *Ala Moana Center* we were so busy walking around amid the crowds of people that we hardly had time for physical contact. And at Makaha Berto was so shy, so afraid to touch because we were so **scantily clad** in only our bathing suits.

I dreamed of Berto on the evening of our ocean adventure, **reenacting** the moments when we lay in **cherubic** innocence next to each other – on the **pristine** island sand, our backs to the warmth of the Hawaiian sun – daydreaming aloud in between moments of reflection and **wonderment**. But even in the dream, we didn't touch one another. It would have been too sudden, too intense for either of us.

Friday evening marked a new chapter in our relationship. Berto and I held hands as we walked to *Baskin-Robbins* for a cone and then to the *Waikiki Twin Theaters*. We were not even sure which movies were playing, but as I walked proudly beside my *Romeo* – ice cream in one hand – I forgot all about our destination.  Instead, I had a deep desire to just lean my head on his shoulder as we walked.  But I was afraid it might **discompose** him.

Before I could think further, Berto leaned *his* head on *my* shoulder!  My eyes closed as I felt the warmth of his upper body rubbing against mine.  Taller than me by three or four inches, Berto rested against me as if I were a **downy** pillow.  The sensation was **mutually** enjoyable; I was his support, he was my support.  For him, I must have represented the first close friend he'd found in the islands.  For me, he was like a younger brother **safeguarding** his dearest companion.

But I was equally confused.  Our date seemed more like a **sibling** get-together.  Were we girlfriend and boyfriend or just two close friends?  I soon accepted that it really didn't matter; the feeling between us was so **captivatingly enrapturing** that I was honored to spend the night with him, friend or boyfriend.

The movie came and went so fast that I didn't remember much about it.  Berto sat **engrossed** in the show, whispering to me occasionally to **illuminate arcane** references I may not have fully grasped while I, on the other hand, was **riveted** in **rhapsodic reverie envisaging** my **winsome beau** sitting next to me holding my hand and sharing his spirit.

"Janet, do you believe in *Bruheria*?"

"Oh, I guess so."

"Isn't it bizarre?"

"Yeah, I guess so."

"And what about the guy with the funny eyes?  He's really 'rad,' huh?"

"Yeah, I guess so."

Our conversation might have sounded **vapid** and **banal** to anyone overhearing us, but every word Berto said was magic to my ears.  And my repetitious replies seemed to energize him even further.  It was the best movie I'd ever seen, and I don't even know what it was all about!

As the final credits flashed by and people began crowding out through the aisles, Berto asked    the **inevitable** question that everyone asks after seeing a good movie:  "Do you want to see it again?"

"Sure,"  I replied cheerfully, expecting to head to the refreshment counter for popcorn and then return to our seats for the next showing.  But Berto had other ideas.

"Good, how about next Friday?"

I was taken **aback** by his innocence, as though he'd never thought of just staying for the next performance. He simply wanted to see me again. That was the real reason for his question, and I didn't want to make him feel foolish by suggesting the obvious.

"Okay," I answered politely, "that would be fun." For an instant I assumed that he would want to invite a bunch of friends along, but this was Berto, not Tony. Maybe Jackie would come along, but that would be all. I wouldn't be entertaining the 'gang.'

We strolled out the exit door and onto the side street alongside Kuhio Avenue, the main road. It was there that the fireworks began.

I know that Berto's **wholesome** presence has **rankled** several of the boys at Ocean View. That usually happens when a mild-mannered newcomer catches the **fancy** of the girls while their boyfriends observe from the sidelines. And Berto's notably good looks sure haven't **endeared** him to the many boys who react more out of jealousy than envy.

It just so happened that Billy Buckovey and a couple of his **cronies** had also gone to see *The Believers* and had left shortly before us. As we passed through the exit door, they spotted us. Billy **initiated** the **impugnation**.

"Hey, Janet, how's it going? Oh, I see. You've dropped Tony to court the new stallion, huh?" Billy and Tony were close friends, so I knew Tony would be **apprised** of my new boyfriend, if he hadn't indeed already suspected the obvious.

Berto tugged **beseechingly** on my arm, motioning for us to turn the other way. But Billy persisted with his **provocation**.

"What's the matter? Your stud doesn't have a tongue?" Billy had been drinking – his **ruthless abandon**, **aimless bravado** and unsteady steps **attested** to that.

Roberto took a deep breath and blew the air up toward the front of his hair, as if to cool himself off. Billy reacted hotly to the response.

"What's your problem, stud? Am I making you sweat or something? Or maybe that's the way you always breathe, huh?" The boys with him started laughing, **deriding** the soft-spoken boy's attempt to avoid a **confrontation**. I could feel Berto begin to tremble. I thought he was scared out of his wits. I couldn't have been more wrong.

Berto began his defense without any further **prodding** or teasing. "You got a problem, punk?" he asked **unabashedly**.

Billy's eyes opened wide. Berto had offered him exactly what he didn't expect to hear. Billy Buckovey weighed a **hefty** 180 pounds, fully fifty pounds more than Berto. The added weight was equally divided between his stomach and arms. One was somewhat the result of fat, but his arms

*"Oh, I see. You've dropped Tony to court the new stallion, huh?"*

31

were muscular, weight-lifter's arms. Berto didn't look as though he'd have a chance, not against Billy, surely not against Billy and his two oversized friends.

Berto continued. "I'm not looking for trouble, bud, but one more big-mouth word and you'll be spitting out your teeth."

Billy started to react **mockingly**, until the final words were spoken. They were not a threat to be taken lightly. Billy was obviously proud of his pearly whites, and the thought of spitting them out quickly **quelled** his **hauteur** and **hubris** and restored in him an uncharacteristic **humility**. His next words were chosen carefully.

"Maybe I've been drinking too much. Let's just forget it, okay?" Then he lifted his left hand and pointed at Berto. "But one day..." he began with renewed **vitality**, his eyes **glaring**. Yet as quickly as he began, he stopped and put the hand down.

I turned to look at Berto. Something had happened between the two, something I didn't catch on to, some **indiscernible** communication, and suddenly the threat ceased.

Billy's next words were somewhere out of the *Twilight Zone*. "No problem, friend. Let's just leave it here. You're a pretty good guy."

"Thanks, Billy," Berto replied **amicably**.

Billy then turned around and walked out to the main street, avoiding passing Berto and me, his friends accompanying him in silent **procession**.

Once the three were out of sight, I ran my hands through my hair, **stupefied** and totally disbelieving what I'd witnessed. "What happened?" I asked **incredulously**.

"I guess we're friends," Berto replied **nonchalantly**, staring out in the direction where the three headed.

"But how?" I couldn't frame the words in any other, more **subtle** way.

"I guess it's in the eyes," Berto answered mechanically, turning and looking straight at me.

He was right. And now I was a believer.

## CHAPTER IX
### *It Started With Baseball*

I knew Janet was seeing Berto Gonzalez. I could tell by the way she would **ogle** him and how she seemed to avoid me at all costs. Billy's words were no surprise to me, though I still don't know why he didn't stick up for me when he saw them at the movies. But like he said, Janet isn't his girlfriend, so he didn't want to get involved. If he'd have been with his Demon friends, he could have really shown that guy a thing or two, but I guess I don't blame him for playing it cool, especially with his own girlfriend there.

The Christmas prom is less than two weeks away, and I'm wondering whether Janet still wants to go. I tried to apologize to her – to tell her that I was sorry for becoming so **riled** – but she's just been avoiding going anywhere near me. Maybe I haven't tried hard enough, either. I want to patch things up between us, but as soon as I get the nerve I forget the words and then just clam up altogether.

When I asked my dad whether it's okay to slap a girl, he instantly became **irate** and **lambasted** me, telling me that if he ever sees me hit my mom he'll throw me out of the house. He didn't even let me explain who I meant, though it really wouldn't have mattered anyway. He and mom have been married for fifteen years, and I guess if anyone has the right to hit mom, it should be him.

I would have asked my mom for advice about what I did, or maybe about how I should try to make up with Janet, but she's always been suspicious of my activities since I joined the Demons and came home wearing the blue cross – symbol of the group. I told her about all the bizarre things we were planning – just fantasies which we'd probably never do, like camping out and drinking beer on the North Shore or kidnapping a tourist and holding him for ransom. I shouldn't have been so bold to her. I was grounded for a week, and my mom has been watching me closely ever since, trying to stop me from becoming "a **hoodlum**."

I feel really odd inside. I want to straighten myself out but I can't. I tried to stop smoking, but instead I started "dipping" – chewing on *Redman* and *Copenhagen* tobacco – and have been getting more and more hooked on a habit that brings me less and less satisfaction. It's hard to keep friends when you've got to spit every fifteen seconds. On the bus, I've had to carry a cup along as a **spittoon**. It's really disgusting, but I do it. In fact, I'm doing a lot of disgusting things and I don't even seem to care. I know that what I'm doing is leading me down a dead-end street, but I can't seem to control my actions. I do think that expressing my thoughts is helping somewhat, however. I got the idea of talking to myself by seeing that new kid who writes all the time. Berto must be writing about something and it's obviously helping him manage through his uncertain times. There seems to be some **curative** value in expressing oneself through words, in facing one's problems and working out possible solutions. It sure beats facing the **futility** of a life that offers no opportunity for **redemption** or **salvation**, and that's what I'm staring at right now.

I've always wanted to be a 'regular guy,' to do something with my life that's **beneficial**, not destructive. But nobody's there to help. I wish the teachers would be more supportive and accommodating, but they just seem to be in their own **parochial** world, **complaisant** to one another but brutal as animal trainers to us. And turning to my folks for advice is equally **unavailing**. To them I'm incapable of asking serious questions and having real problems. Their replies always amount to the same advice: "Go out and play and stay out of trouble." That's fine for a five-year-old, but it's meaningless for a guy my age.

I don't have anyone to talk with anymore. In the past Janet was there for me, but in each other's constant company we soon tired of relating to one another. Maybe that was my fault. Maybe I just listened too much to my **knavish kinsmen** who only saw girls as objects of **conquest** and who egged me on to 'go for it,' expressing their **domineeringly chauvinistic** goal in a **plethora** of **ribald** and **lascivious innuendos**. After a while, I saw Janet as nothing more than a mere object of **lust** there for me to display my **virility** and masculine **prowess** in front of others. I could see myself performing for the gang, not for myself. And I lost Janet as a result.

I've seriously thought about leaving the Demons, but I'm afraid. I never thought I'd admit this to myself, but I'm really scared of my friends. When I was six or seven, I used to play with all the guys and have a good time with them, but as I grew older I began to discover a new word: "competition." At first it meant demonstrating and exhibiting our abilities. The little league baseball games were a lighthearted battle between teams. Everybody had fun, though it was more fun to win than to lose. I didn't mind losing, however; after all, we were friends.

The competitive **amity** began to disappear as time passed. I began to notice that some of my **adversarial** counterparts were being pressured by their parents to win, to be 'better than everyone else.' And I began to see these **insidious** pressures affect their attitudes. What used to be **innocuous revelry** was now becoming a not-so-friendly **rivalry**, a small war.

My first **melee** came when I was nine years old, during a baseball game against the *Kapahulu Raiders*. The opposing team was leading 4-3 in the sixth inning and I was on third base, representing the tying run. James Kirshel, our pitcher, was batting and there was only one out.

After a couple of attempted bunts, James swung all the way and put the next pitch high into left. As the outfielder prepared to make the catch and throw to home, I got ready to tag up, excited that I could make it a brand new, tie ballgame. I heard both teams yelling frantically, the opposing groups of parents equally **animated**.

The fielder caught the ball, and the race for home began. I tore furiously for the plate, the ball coming ever nearer. I knew it was going to be close, and I was prepared to slide as best I knew how.

The catcher awaited, looking scared and anxious, trying desperately to block the plate. The noise around us increased, and every stride seemed to take forever. My slide was like slow-motion, the ball arriving a split-second before me. I tucked my head down as my left foot struck out for the safety zone, and then everything went black for a moment. I had rammed into the catcher, who fell on top of me as we both struggled in our own efforts – mine to be safe and his to tag me out. Dust

*I knew it was going to be close...*

flew all around us, and when I opened my eyes I stared up searchingly at the umpire for a sign. The catcher was also eagerly seeking the judgment from the grownup.

"Safe," he replied, making the appropriate signal with his hands.

The **volatile** crowd erupted, half applauding in **jubilant exultation** and half shouting in **acerbic aspersion**. The catcher had tagged me, but the ball had fallen out from his glove. I was clearly safe.

"Lousy call," one of the parents **railed** from the bleachers. "You're an idiot."

I looked up at the stands and **espied** a **stately** gentleman dressed in a handsome leisure suit and sporting an **ascot**. His **acrimonious** name-calling seemed totally out of place, but then it dawned on me just how passionate the fans were about our little league game. The competitive pressure had apparently been building throughout the game, climaxing with this uncomfortably embarrassing scene staged by the parents themselves.

The umpire remained **unruffled** throughout the **volley** of rude remarks; he had obviously heard them many times before. I picked myself up, shook off the dust and began to walk towards the dugout. But as I left, I **inadvertently** tripped over the catcher's foot and fell to the ground again. Several onlookers yelled encouragement to me as though implying he had tripped me on purpose. I turned to face the boy, just to see if he would apologize. Their **goading** grew louder; the parents were now taking sides, as though the catcher and I were ready to **engage** in **fisticuffs**. But we weren't. Instead, we looked gazingly at one another, and he spoke first.

"Sorry, pal. I hope you didn't get hurt."

"No," I replied quietly, "I'm okay. How about you?"

"Yeah, I'm okay. You really barreled into me. What a mess." He laughed softly, just loud enough for me to hear.

"I'm still wearing the dust," I smiled back.

"Don't let him talk to you like that," one of the **rabble** of **pugnacious** parents called out. Neither of us knew whom the words were meant for. We both turned toward the **truculent** adult.

Our team-benches then began slowly clearing, players heading cautiously in our direction as if preparing themselves **preliminarily** for a **protracted row**.

"My name's Tony," I said as I faced the catcher.

"I'm Danny," he replied **affably**.

We started to offer our hands in friendship but were interrupted by a roar from beyond.

"Hey, take your hands off my kid," one **rankled** father **vociferated**.

Before our hands could meet, Danny's father pulled me **ungraciously** away, shoving me to the ground. As I fell, I could hear him **chastising** his son for dropping the ball. I felt as though I were in the middle of the land of giants, all the adults crowding in with the players. Then, just as I was about to get up, one boy kicked me in the face and I toppled backwards into another player from the opposing side. He was visibly **irked** and, being twice my size, wasted no time in demonstrating his disapproval.

"Twerp, you think you're hot stuff," the **rival retorted** as he proceeded to pick me up to take a full swing at me. Luckily, I managed to duck. As his hand passed over me, I lashed out and caught him squarely on his jaw. My wrist ached from the **percussion**, but before he could react we were separated by a couple of adults, and the conflict was over.

From that incident I learned that fighting offered me no glamour, only sprained knuckles. But the event showed me just how far removed from 'fun' a game could become, because of adults. And from that day I became aware of a fierce competition between people. Some, like Danny, could shake it off, but for most of the boys, especially the bigger ones, competition marked the surest way to gain approval from the adults and the perfect excuse to **kindle** a feud or a **skirmish**, something the 'grownup boys' seemed to take great delight in. For me, it was what I wanted most to avoid.

I didn't play in any organized sports after that year. I told my folks that such activities were boring, though that wasn't the real reason. I was afraid, not afraid of the sports themselves but of the people. I was safe when I was alone. I began to spend time playing video games and hanging around the playgrounds, away from leagues and other organized events.

As I grew older I became aware of yet another threatening organization: street gangs. They were popping up everywhere, and I couldn't avoid them. I knew I'd one day be pitted against them, not unless I joined with them first.

I've been a Dark Demon for a little over a year now, and it's shielded me from the threat of fights. I've found safety in the group, though I must admit I haven't found any friends there. I've become a 'big man,' the symbol of strength and leadership, but I know I'm only doing whatever keeps me from having to compete against the others. I can face up to adults now because of my gang **affiliation**; they know better than to attempt to challenge a gang of teenagers. I can **defy** them, **levy imprecations** against them and even **effectuate opprobrious** and **vandalous desecration** right in front of their eyes, but they'll never **requite** or seek to stop me. Adults know better than to tangle with **scurrilous incorrigibles** like me.

What is it that makes teenage gang members so **impetuous** and **foolhardy**? When I was alone I was careful not to get into too much trouble. But now, as a Demon, I feel I have no limits. Instead of **erring** on the side of caution, I'm **possessed** to show that I'm better and meaner than anyone else. It's as though I'm trying to live up to the image of a gang member for the sake of my **peers**, the same way the little leaguers tried to live up to the expectations of their dads.  I guess a teenage gang is just an extension of the little league because the goals are the same: to be the best, the most feared and respected.  But gangs take the game one step further, using bats for more **sinister** purposes against the opposition.

Parents don't go around fighting each other, so why do they encourage us little leaguers to go around doing it?  Could it be that our parents are afraid of us, and rather than have us fight against them when we grow bigger and stronger, they'd rather have us fight each other?  Does that make sense?  I really don't know, but it scares me somehow.  I feel that I'm in the middle of a battlefield, and unless I stick with the gang I'll become a victim of their **misguided** beliefs, the result of their folks' encouragement which they've turned into **antagonistically aggressive** action.

But while I've found safety in the gang, I think I've lost Janet at the same time.  I really think she's forgotten me, given up on me and gone for a more suitable boyfriend.  And I don't blame her.  I'm just all screwed up, sitting here under a tree, thinking out loud and wondering where it's all leading to.  I want to chew, but it's messing up my mind.  The tobacco is making my gums bleed, and I'm so irritable all the time.  I really don't know what I'm doing anymore.  Maybe it's the end, maybe I'm about to fall off the edge and just drop out.  But I don't want to drop out.  I want someone to give a damn about me.  And yet, I don't even seem to give a damn about myself.  Maybe I do, but I just don't know how to get myself together.  What do I do?  God, what do I do?

*What do I do?*

# CHAPTER X
## *A Strange Experience*

The past two weeks have really gone by quickly, perhaps because there is so much to do here in Hawaii that one is always busy. I also think, however, it's because the island lifestyle is so easygoing and time is not one's **nemesis** that one can pursue one's own chosen path **heedless** of and **oblivious** to the **constraints** of time. In short, time passes quickly when you're having fun.

I saw a great movie with Janet the other day. I'd seen it before, but this time it seemed more magical. As planned earlier, we met in Waikiki at 6:00 on Friday evening, Janet looking as **gorgeous** as always. Besides her good looks, what makes her the **nonpareil** is her **distinctive** and **inimitable** down-to-earth **demeanor**. She's so natural and such a good listener. I was going to take Jake along but changed my mind at the last minute, telling him that I was going out afterwards and wouldn't be home until midnight. He was **crestfallen** and somewhat **galled**, but that's because I'd been talking about the show all week. If he had known earlier of my change of heart, he'd have **disported** in a **diversion** of merriment with his **frolicsome** friends after school and likely stayed out well beyond the **gloaming**. I'm sure he'll get over it, though. He's probably got a million things to do and places to go tomorrow, so he sure doesn't need me to **shepherd** him or keep him occupied. Not like back in Owry.

Janet and I have been going together for about a month. I even presented her with a ring last week. I waited until we were in the movie theater before I surprised her with it. It cost me twenty dollars, and I had to run errands for my mom all week to earn the money. In Owry I'd have simply gone into a jewelry shop and **absconded** with the ring, but since coming to Hawaii I haven't felt **compelled** to cross that line. I'm sure other guys do it, but that's their personal **peccadillo**, not mine.

I offered the ring to Janet in a most **unorthodox** manner. I asked her to show me her hands, which I said were the most beautiful I'd ever seen.

"Gee, you're real sweet," she replied **coyly**.

"What could possibly make those hands look even prettier?" I questioned suggestively.

Janet answered with a **quizzical** look, but before any words could form I **subtly** stroked my hand over hers. As our fingertips gently touched one another I slipped the ring **surreptitiously** onto her finger. At first it was loose, but as it slid deeper it felt **snug**.

I then sang along softly to a song that was being played over the movie speakers, a song that seemed so appropriate for the occasion:

> *"We connect, when we're together it's so perfect;*
> *The way you shock me with your white hot love,*
> *I start to overload,*
> *I explode when we connect..."*

"Gee, you're wonderful," Janet whispered **dulcetly** in my ear, then proceeding to run her tongue against it and give me a kiss that made my skin prickle. I don't think I'd ever had a girl kiss me like that before, except in my most **erotically fanciful** dreams. I was glad Jake hadn't come along.

"Do you want to go somewhere else?" I asked tenderly, wondering whether she was expecting more from me now that we had sealed a friendship that went deeper than casual.

"If you want to, Berto. But it's up to you." Her reply was so **guileless** and undemanding that I felt no urgency to **stoke** the fire to a white-hot flame. There would be **ample** opportunity for our feelings to grow.

We stayed for the entire movie, Janet choosing to lean gently upon my shoulder – her hand and mine clasped tightly together, resting upon my lap. I felt as though I were in a dream; it was the nicest, most **sublime** evening I'd ever spent in my whole life.

That night, I put away my six-inch blade, the one reminder of Owry County that I carried wherever I went. I had found a place where it wasn't necessary, and I knew I could find peace of mind without any weapon to protect me. This place was my new home, the fears of the past no longer a **spectral bugbear** influencing my actions. I was safe and enjoying every moment; the knife would no longer be needed.

It's funny how things happen when you don't expect them to. Before we moved to Hawaii, I was trying to score with another girl, Christine. She was the town flirt, and the Downtown Damned were pressuring me to go out with her.

"What's the matter, 'Shiloh'? You don't have any **cajones**?" The gang loved to **taunt** and **gibe** whenever **opportune** moments **availed** themselves, and anyone who wished to survive the streets learned to **indulge** such comments and react with a **smirk** or **retaliate** with one's own **badinage**. But the pressure and the **badgering** continued, day after day.

I finally **succumbed** to the gang's **pestering** and **mustered** enough courage to ask Christine out one evening, hoping that we'd be able to find a warm room or den where I could prove myself to the gang. But the **inauspicious** evening **stymied** my attempts. My folks were home and so were hers. So we spent the time at *McDonald's* nibbling on french fries while trying to find words to replace actions. Nothing happened. It was a long, cold, boring evening, and I never went out with the **coquettish** lass again.

Everything developed differently, however, on my date with Janet. I'd started the evening only interested in having an innocent time, but by the end of the night we'd exchanged **sensuous** kisses and had begun a relationship far beyond what I'd ever expected. The ring was a gift for her, but the **fervent** friendship we were **nurturing** went far beyond what such an offering usually **betokened**.

And I experienced it all without anyone else telling me what to do. We had discovered one another by ourselves, just as *Romeo* had met *Juliet*. Indeed, the evening was truly **divinely preordained**.

This week has really gone by quickly. Almost too quickly. I have hardly had time to write, and yet I've got so much to say. Next week is the prom dance, and my mom said she'll drive us there and pick us up. I don't mind getting a free ride there, but after the dance we may not want to come straight home. So I've left the after-dance plans open-ended just in case. Janet's been so quiet about it, though. She really seems eager to go, but in class she avoids talking about it; in fact, she seems to be avoiding any lengthy conversation with me altogether. I think her other friends may be teasing her about me, especially since I'm new in school and don't have very many friends – not many at all, come to think of it. And yet, I'm enjoying every minute in school, carefully **cultivating** my own **coterie** and **navigating** my own destiny. Life is sure different here than back in Owry County.

I shared in a strange experience with one boy in my history class today. I think he used to be Janet's boyfriend. It's hard to explain what really happened. I'm not sure if I helped him or hurt him. He's really a messed-up person. I can't figure him out. Maybe the Hawaiian sunshine has fried his brains.

We were taking a test in Mrs. Amagone's class – a chapter test covering the Roman Empire – and everyone was **sedulously** answering the essay questions, when I heard noises coming from a few desks away. There was Tony casually carving out something on the empty desk in front of him. The distraction was an obvious bother to everyone, and Mrs. A. had no trouble detecting and tracing the source of the cracking wood. Tony must have been crazy to do that during an exam, especially since knives aren't even permitted in school. He was just asking to get himself busted. I'd never seen anyone act so idiotically before. In Owry, we only did what we knew we could get away with. Doing something simply for the **clamor** of attention was unheard of. We had learned to become survivors, not **masochistic martyrs**. Tony's actions were **pathetic**. I felt sorry for him.

I remember my first meeting with Tony. It was two days after the school year first started. He was a completely different person then. He politely introduced himself to me and we exchanged a hearty handshake. He then told me about his gang, the Dark Demons, and bragged about all the things they were doing. Most of the **antics** sounded silly, like painting graffiti on walls and making trouble for tourists. I laughed along with him and thanked him for the information but didn't advance the conversation any further.

At that time Tony seemed **self-assured** and acted somewhat **brash**, as though he were **infallible** and riding on top of the world. His height and build matched mine almost evenly, and I envied his sunny and carefree **disposition**, though not his being leader of a gang. I'd already graduated from that scene.

But in the past three months, I witnessed some major changes coming over him. He started smoking during lunch, and his hair soon began to appear **disheveled** and matted. In fact, it was as though he'd stopped caring for himself altogether. He would come to class appearing **languorous**

*I remember my first meeting with Tony...He was a completely different person then.*

and hung over, and I could see in him a growing **listlessness** that was slowly distancing himself from his **fractious** flock. Yet, he always appeared to be ever **mindful** of my presence, as though I continued to represent some attraction to him. Whether as friend or **foe**, he always glanced my way as I entered and exited the class, even though we rarely spoke with one another. I sometimes nodded my head to acknowledge his presence, but he always declined to **reciprocate**. He simply stared **vacantly** back at me, a look which grew hazier as the weeks passed. I could see that he was slowly dropping out. I'd seen it happen to guys back home, those who'd taken to drugs or heavy **intoxication**. Tony had gotten hooked on something.

My suspicions were confirmed when I began to see him carrying along a cup, a cheap **spittoon**. He was chewing tobacco – and for a boy his age, that's **analogous** to an adult who is on hard liquor. Maybe he was doing more than just chewing, perhaps he was taking uppers and downers with it. The two often went hand-in-hand in Owry, reflecting a weakness or a frustration in a person who would take anything to try to **palliate** the effects of depression or **malaise**.

Tony's **comportment deteriorated** as the semester progressed, but this wood-carving episode had taken him beyond the point of no return. He really needed somebody to help him out. Mrs. A. was certainly not going to **condone** such actions or make life any easier for him.

"Where's that **abominable** noise coming from?" the teacher **bellowed** in her **authoritarian** un-feminine voice. Of course, everyone knew the source but no one uttered a sound. Tony, however, kept carving, either totally absorbed in his artwork or totally committed to a **crucifixion**.

"All right, Mr. Renaldo, come here. Right now!" Her voice was rising, and the class braced itself for **unbridled pandemonium**. The test wasn't important anymore.

Tony looked up **groggily** from his desk, and I could tell he was on something. His eyes were glassy and his reflexes were slow. He appeared helplessly **embroiled** in an **inextricable** path doomed to **perdition**, and even Janet couldn't help him now. I glanced quickly at her, but she didn't notice me. She was looking down at her exam, perhaps **indifferent** to the **chaos** or else not wanting to add **kindling** to the **incendiary inferno**.

I myself couldn't just watch **passively** and see what would **befall** Tony. I was once in a similar situation, and I knew how it felt to be alone, in an **inimical** world of passionless strangers. I'd experienced that same fear and loneliness the weekend I spent in the **juvenile** cellblock only a few short months ago.

I can well remember the **eeriness** of entering the cell, a twelve-foot-square room with only a double-bunk-bed, a toilet and sink. It looked like one of those **dingy** hotel rooms out of an old black-and-white movie. There was a barred window which let in a small amount of sunlight, but all in all the cell was **grim** and **forbidding**. As I was led through the cell door and the handcuffs were removed, I wondered how many boys before me had journeyed through its doors, and how many had begun a life of crime at this stage. I couldn't help but think to myself just how ineffective such facilities are in **forestalling** crime. All they do is scare a person into believing that he's got no choice but to become a criminal, as if the walls are saying "Welcome, and we know you'll be back." Those were the last words I wanted to hear, but undoubtedly they were the ones I'd be hearing the most from everyone I met.

As my hands were rescued from the metal cuffs, I turned to the guard and said, almost automatically, "Thank you."

The guard looked at me with a **bemused** expression and replied "For what?" He was right. There was nothing to thank anyone for. Being in jail was no reward.

There was one other person in my cell, but as he lay motionless on the lower bunk I sensed his **willful** isolation, his detachment from everything around him. I would have introduced myself, but his obvious disinterest in my presence, together with the cold response from the guard, alerted me not to act too friendly to anyone. No one had come here to talk about anything. The place was cold and **inhospitable**. It was jail.

I huddled **inconspicuously** against one corner – across from the bunk and near the sink – afraid to disturb the person who was lying on the bed but not sure where else I could go. The guy appeared to be about my age, but he was very big. I suspected that he'd tower above me if he were standing, and his quiet **air** was a warning for me not to make any contact with him. I'd remembered the **adage** that the quiet person is the one to fear the most, and this silent stranger seemed to **epitomize** the point, like the most **pernicious** of **predators** who **stalk** in silence. I didn't want to find out why he was in the jail or for how long. He had his own problems; I had mine. And the more I kept mine to myself, the better chance I'd have to survive. I was learning the rules very quickly.

"Hey, you across the way," an inmate from another cell whispered my way, breaking the short peace I was experiencing as I rested quietly against the wall. I turned to see if the words were addressed to me. Two arms wrapped around a cell door across the corridor, and between them I could make out a rather **dour** and **sullen** unshaven man.

"You hear me?" he questioned somewhat threateningly.

"Yeah," I replied, uncertain what more I should say. I stood up before him, and he continued.

"What's your name?" the stranger demanded.

"Uh...Roberto..." I didn't know whether I should offer up an **assumed** name, but since it was only my first name anyway I didn't figure there would be any harm in telling the truth. Besides, I had a deep, conscious fear that, should I be caught lying to another inmate, I would doubtless find myself in an **imminent imbroglio**. Even with bars separating the inmates, a jail cell was no **refuge** or **sanctuary**, and as I began to talk with *Jack the Ripper* on the other side, I could feel myself trembling in **abject** terror.

*Two arms wrapped around a cell door across the corridor, and between them I could make out a rather dour and sullen unshaven man.*

"Do you know who I am, Roberto?" The voice was slow, **deliberate** and filled with **malign** confidence.

I felt my throat grow raw, as though a grapefruit were lodged in it.

"No, sir." I chose the words carefully. I could feel my body contracting, my muscles losing their power as though I were about to faint. I suddenly needed to use the bathroom, and my heart began to pulsate furiously. I felt helpless, totally at the mercy of the **inscrutable** force behind the other bars.

"I'm B.B. Know what that stands for?"

My mind flashed through a million possibilities. Billy Boy, Big Boy, Bad Boy, Brahma Bull, Bone Bruiser, Baby Blue...the list was endless, and I was so scared I couldn't remember whether the tone of his voice invited a reply or whether any answer would be received angrily. I took a chance.

"Brad Baldwin?" The name just came from out of left field. It was the least offensive answer I could **conjure** up.

"What?" the bearded person asked, **chafed** at the perceived **impudence**.

I hurried a follow-up answer. "No, I really don't know, sir."

"Well, I'll tell you. It stands for 'B.B.' Understand?" He **chortled demonically** and **derisively**, then suddenly stopped, as though the joke were over.

I was frozen in fear, **petrified** by the pointlessness of the **malefactor's manipulation**. I got the point: no questions, no answers; just mind your own business and don't act wise. The bitter truth was so obvious, yet I was not in attendance to **unravel** life's **esoteric enigmas**. I was in jail, and I **pined** for a path out of this private **purgatory**.

"You still listening to me, Roberto?" His voice was now hard and **gruff**.

My silence had obviously disturbed him more. I felt cornered, unable to defend myself and yet forced to answer. Just hearing my name said so slowly, so threateningly made me fear for my life. B.B. was no wimp. He was for real. I wondered if the **hulking** brute in the lower bunk was another B.B. I didn't want to find out.

"Yes, sir, I'm still here." The words might have sounded **frivolously mundane** in any other occasion, but now they came out serious, dead serious. I needed to make friends with him; I needed to **ensure** my survival so I might one day get out and stay out, a million miles away from B.B. all that **festered** in his presence.

"I want you to do me a favor," the inmate said **solicitously**.

My heart fluttered amid the wild **palpitations**.  The request presented itself as a most **fortuitous** opportunity for me to **stem** any **lingering ill will** between us and **quell** my own **qualms**, but I knew it wasn't going to be a simple favor.  I couldn't say "No" but I was afraid to say "Yes."

"Okay," I replied **guardedly**, my voice cracking as though I were still going through puberty.

"You're a nice boy, Roberto.  I think we'll be good friends."

I felt somewhat **disencumbered** and relieved.  Maybe I had indeed **ingratiated** myself with the **imposing adversary**.  My heart rate slowed down and my muscles relaxed.

B.B. didn't say anything for a few moments. The Hulk hadn't flinched either, and I felt as though time had temporarily stood still.

"Here's what I want you to do," he began at last.  "There's a **gruesome** giant in the cell with you, right?"

"Yeah," I replied **timidly**, not wishing to **affront** my cellmate and yet certainly not intending to offend B.B.

"Okay, here's what you do.  Tell him that the time's 9:30.  Got it?  9:30."

I knew the time was closer to five or six, but I didn't dare to correct him.  The time was obviously related to some future event, though I had no desire to learn more about it.  I moved quietly to the **bovine** brute and tapped him on the shoulder.  He didn't react.  I then whispered in his ear "9:30, the time's 9:30." Suddenly he turned around to face me, opened his eyes, opened his mouth as if to say something, and then spit on me, right between my eyes.  I fell backwards as far away as I could pull myself until I hit the bars of the door.  I sank to the floor, paralyzed and **incapacitated**, unable even to move my hands to wipe off my face.

Every **transgression** I'd ever committed flashed before my eyes, as though this were my hellish punishment for existing.  Logic had no meaning.  Everything was in a **flux**.  I was totally in shock and totally out of control.  I began to cry, the tears flowing without end, carrying with them the gob of humiliation that moved down my face.  I tried to **bridle** my emotions but the tears gushed as I first **whimpered**, then sobbed loudly, B.B. all the while laughing **sardonically** in the other cell.

"So sorry, Roberto," he added in a **mockingly** apologetic manner, "That's just the way things are. But I'll tell you truthfully," he continued from the other side of the hall, "I tell everyone the same thing. Banana breath is so stupid, but he hates it when anyone says 9:30 to him.  You're the fourth guy this week.  Nothing personal.  Just for kicks.  Didn't think you'd cry, though."

B.B.'s voice softened a bit.  "Really, Roberto, you're a nice boy.  Really nice and friendly.  And I bet you're cute, too."

The sobs stopped instantly.  I was now in a state of panic, seized by a **maelstrom** of emotions. Everything I said and did was being **distorted** and **perverted** to meet B.B.'s **whims**.  I was in a

*Catch-22* position, and everything I said – or didn't say – just got me more deeply **mired** in a **morass** of moral **depravity**.

I stood up and faced the other cell.  Now I was speaking to literally save my life.  "B.B., you keep your filthy thoughts to yourself.  Hear me, B.B.?"  I didn't want to yell at him, but I needed to **convey** my point **succinctly** and **unequivocally**.  I was ready for anything he might say.

"Okay, Roberto, okay.  I hear you."  The conversation was over.  B.B. didn't push the issue any further, and we spent the remainder of the hour in silence.  I had apparently **defused** the situation  and felt calm enough to get some rest; I fell asleep leaning against the cell bars.

✩ ✩ ✩ ✩ ✩ ✩ ✩ ✩ ✩ ✩ ✩ ✩ ✩ ✩ ✩ ✩ ✩ ✩ ✩ ✩ ✩ ✩ ✩ ✩ ✩ ✩ ✩ ✩ ✩ ✩ ✩ ✩ ✩ ✩ ✩ ✩ ✩

"Dinner time.  Get your worthless selves up and out.  Let's go."  The guard's shouts woke me up instantly.  I could see the **obtuse** Hulk rise up automatically, then move **torpidly** out the door, **oblivious** to my presence.  He was totally spaced out.  I followed momentarily, first washing my  face and cleaning my eyes to hide the **residue** of my tears.

The walk to the cafeteria was carefully patrolled, each cell opened separately to avoid excessive **mingling** between inmates.  Those not dressed appropriately were given shirt and long pants, apparently a special requirement to eat with all the other "guests."  As a result, everyone in the hall looked the same, with baggy grey overalls and **plaid** pullovers.  The premises were kept under **stringent** supervision, with few liberties extended to any inmate.  I knew I would be there for a couple of days at most, but as I entered the room and viewed forty other **miscreants** I realized that it would not be wise for me to **peer** too far into the future; I needed to watch my back every moment I remained behind bars.  Observing boys with scars and other reminders of past experiences, I was unmistakably aware that I might come out on time but with a few teeth missing.  I had no scars or tattoos and didn't **yearn** to witness firsthand any such initiation during dinner. I was determined to hold my own and stay out of trouble.

"You sit there," one guard directed as I approached a table, plate of corn hash in hand.  I was seated in between a couple of thin, ordinary-looking kids.  They looked friendly enough, but I had already experienced enough surprises in my brief **sojourn** in hell not to assume anything.  I sat down with my plate and said nothing.  I was there to eat, with no interest to do anything else.

I learned an **invaluable** lesson during my two days at the Owry County Juvenile Corrections Facility.  I discovered what loneliness is, what self-preservation is all about, and what it really means to have a friend when all else seems hopeless.

I had a friend at the Facility: I had myself.  But as I watched Tony in Mrs. A.'s class, I could see a boy who had no friends at that moment.  I saw instead a **wretched**, **forlorn** and **forsaken** fellow human being who desperately needed a friend.  And I knew that I couldn't just sit back and watch Tony go through the humiliation I had once suffered.  Mrs. A. was prepared to barbecue the boy, and I could feel my heart pumping faster in anticipation.  I could feel my body sweating as though I myself were back behind bars.  I wanted to help Tony as badly as anything I'd done since I'd first arrived in Hawaii.

# CHAPTER XI
## *Deciding On The Prom*

Tony really freaked out yesterday. I want to write about it, but I'm still not sure what happened. And I'm not even sure he's going to come back to school next week.

Until yesterday, I thought I was finally headed in a new direction, going with Berto and leaving the problems of the past behind. In fact, Berto and I are now going steady. He gave me a beautiful coral ring last Friday – one which must have cost him at least thirty dollars – when we went to the movies. It was truly a magical evening, indeed.

Berto is such an **unpretentious** boy with an **engaging** personality. He has nothing to hide and is always friendly and curious, like a little wind-up doll. He asked me if I wanted to go to the Christmas prom, and I said "Yes." The whole week seemed to be going so smoothly, so wonderfully, until Tony tried to **unceremoniously** steal center-stage during history class.

I never suspected that Tony was falling apart little by little. I thought he was finding himself – he and his **boorish** band of barbaric **bumpkins** — but apparently I was wrong. And I'm still not sure if I might be the reason why he left the island this weekend or how long he'll be gone. I tried to find the graffiti that he etched on the desk, but the only thing I could make out was "I want t-." I think it was Tony's markings but I can't be sure and really don't know what he was trying to say. I seriously expected to find some four-letter **execration** scrawled on the back of the seat, but I didn't find any other traces of writing that looked new or like Tony's style.

From that class my **disposition** changed rather quickly from joyful to **melancholy**, perhaps out of **solicitude** for a person I've cared so much for. I seriously think I'm still in love with Tony; that's the only way I can explain why he seems to be in all my thoughts and why I seem to be more interested in his problems than I am in my happiness with Berto. Or maybe it's that I **derive** a greater sense of purpose assisting in another's problems rather than **wallowing** in my own good fortune.

The whole upsetting affair actually started before class, during morning recess, when I saw Tony and a couple of his **scamps quibbling** over something. He seemed unusually **peevish** and **belligerent**, behaving as though he were ready to fight both the boys over what was being said. I then saw him throw his can of *Pepsi* on the ground and storm away, furious at something the others had said.

When I arrived in class, Tony was already seated. We didn't say anything to one another, but I knew he was stealing glimpses nervously my way. As the class poured in, Tony continued to glance **furtively** in my direction. But he wouldn't stare. His eyes seemed to simply pass by me on the way to looking at something or someone else. I would look up at him when they neared me, but his eyes never met mine. He was afraid to make contact with me, and so I **obliged** by not looking up anymore. I kept my eyes glued to my exam for the remainder of the class, not wishing to disturb any secret stares he might be passing my way.

The history chapter test was **comprehensive** and demanding, and I found myself totally **immersed** in it, unaware what Tony was doing or where he was looking. But then I heard strange noises, like rats nibbling on wood. I wanted to look up, but I had my suspicions as to where they were coming from – so I kept my eyes glued to the exam. The noises grew louder, until Mrs. Amagone spotted the person.

"Come here. Right now," she roared in her **imperious** tone of voice.

I looked up and saw Tony carving something. He stopped slowly, then stared glassy-eyed at the teacher. She was **flaring** at the nostrils, as though Tony had just carved his initials on her car. I could sense that she was **livid** and about to **vent** her **spleen** on him.

Then the strangest thing happened. A desk toppled over near the back of the class, close to the exit. As if having a mind of its own, it **teetered** on one side and then fell over, landing against the side wall. Someone had apparently kicked it, intentionally it seemed. Mrs. Amagone ceased her **impassioned fulmination** and focused instead on the back of the room.

"All right, who did that?" she asked, **befuddled**.

There was no reply.

"Now really, people, what's coming over you? This isn't a circus, you know."

The teacher had been so caught off guard by the bizarre flying desk that she couldn't focus on her anger. She was now more **perplexed** – perhaps even a bit frightened – and **resolved** to restore the class the best she could to some degree of **normalcy**.

"Let's just get back to work, okay? And let's keep our feet off the chairs and our attention on the test."

The distraction changed the whole **complexion** of the class. There was less emphasis on the exam and more on the mystery of the **animated** desk. It was within reach of four different boys, but no one volunteered the name of the person who **perpetrated** the prank. I think I'll ask Berto, since he was one of the four and probably has an idea who was crazy enough to try such a stunt.

Tony didn't carve much after that. I think he tried a little more, but I guess the **startling** desk incident **quashed** his **refractory** rebelliousness. Nevertheless, I realized from that exhibition that something was really bothering him and that I still care about him. In fact, I guess I really care too much.

The reason I had been consciously avoiding Tony recently was because I thought he'd been surviving comfortably on his own, that he was enjoying life – even with his **wrongheaded clique** of **cronies**. But yesterday I understood that things haven't been going well with him, that something

*Then the strangest thing happened.*

really is troubling him, and that I still love him enough to want to share in and help him overcome his personal problems.

I tried to talk with him after class but he disappeared quickly, as though he had somewhere special to go. Or else he just didn't want to see me. And that's what makes me feel so helpless and confused: I just don't know what's happening between Tony and me. Maybe he has other issues that don't involve me. Or perhaps he's going over the deep end from something he's taking? I just don't know. But one thing I do know is that Tony's coming unglued and I've got to try to do something to help him. But what? I don't even know if he likes me anymore, if he even knows I still exist. And it's this **disquieting** uncertainty that is making me feel so **anxious**, so **apprehensive**.

I don't know whether I should go to the prom with Berto. Susan and I discussed the matter after class yesterday.

"It's your decision, Janet," she replied. "It all depends on how much you like him and how much you still like Tony."

"I like Berto a lot, but there's something about Tony that **lures** me to him and all his personal problems."

"Do you love him?"

Susan's question was the **definitive unmitigated query**, demanding an answer of **momentous** proportion. The heart of the matter rested upon whether I am really still in love with Tony. Her question was too uncompromising and my decision too **consequential** to answer **precipitately**. There was no easy answer. It wasn't "Yes," it wasn't "No." From the silence, Susan could sense my **vacillation**.

"All right, so maybe you do a little, right Janet?"

"Yeah, a little I guess." The answer was satisfactory for me and for her. We both realized I hadn't forgotten Tony; now it was only a question of how much I really loved him and wanted to become closer with him. "So what should I tell Berto?" I asked finally.

"You mean about the prom, or about Tony?"

"Maybe a bit of both."

"Go to the prom with him. He asked you. After all, he likes you and you like him. Did Tony ask you to go?" Susan asked **straightforwardly**. I could sense that she already knew how I would respond. "Do you think he'd even want to go if you asked him?"

"Probably not. Even if he wanted to, he'd probably say 'No'."

*"So what should I tell Berto?"  I asked finally.*

"Then what's the problem?" Susan asked. "Looks to me like you've got to let Tony decide for himself what to do. You can't make up his mind. And even if he likes you, he's sure not showing it very well."

I felt like defending him, as though I should **sanction** and **validate** all his **idiosyncrasies** and **foibles**. But Susan and I had been friends since the third grade and she was **conversant** with all my activities involving Tony, including the earliest days in *steal away*. She knew I was completely **baffled** and clueless regarding Tony's recent **outlandish** behavior, and it would have been senseless for me to **feign intimate** insight into his recent behavior.

"Boys are really strange sometimes, aren't they?" I asked **confidentially**.

"Sure are, Janet. But we know that they'll always come back to us, right?"

Her encouragement and optimism felt good. "Yeah, I guess Tony'll call me one day, someday. But the way he looked yesterday, I gotta worry a little."

"Worry a lot. That's what you should do."

"But what else can I do? I mean, should I talk to him or maybe call him?"

"After the prom, perhaps. But not before. It's coming up in one week, so don't put your friendship with Berto on the line. Just be yourself and don't try to do too much."

I knew what Susan was implying. I had become too concerned for anyone's good and needed to let the events take their course, naturally, and then see where everything stood after next week. But I also knew that the coming week was going to be one of the longest of my life; I would need to **dissimulate** my anxiety behind a **façade** of **insouciance** when in the company of Berto, all the while **fretfully mindful** that Tony was a ticking time-bomb ready to explode at any given moment.

"Susan," I asked **spontaneously**, "who are you going to the prom with?" She hadn't said anything to me about her date, so the **probing** question seemed **apt** and **germane**.

"Honestly, Janet? I really don't have one yet. I might ask Georgie or Gerald. Or maybe Stanley. Or maybe Berto." She **tittered** as she mentioned Berto, but I sensed almost **intuitively** that she meant it quite seriously.

"Should I ask Tony?" I interrupted suddenly, unsure whether my latest question seemed appropriate. The words **rekindled** my desire to become involved, despite Susan having just **admonished** me for my **intemperance** and **willful intrusiveness**.

"That's really up to you, Janet," Susan replied somewhat distantly. "But it will only work out if Tony says 'Yes'."

So after all the ideas were **bandied** about, we were back to the same **dilemma**: whether or not I should go to the prom with Berto. But now the decision was no longer between my attending or not attending; rather, it was a matter of deciding whom to go with. I felt relieved and **enlivened** knowing that both Berto and Tony might be at the prom, especially since I really wanted to meet both of them there rather than add to the complications by leaving one out. But how would Berto react to going out with Susan? He hardly knew her at all. The proposal didn't make a whole lot of sense.

"Do you think he'll go with you?" I asked Susan.

"Thanks for the compliment," she **retorted sarcastically**, though understanding that I really didn't intend the question to sound **insolent**.

"No, I didn't mean it that way, Susan. I only meant–"

"I know, I know. Don't worry, I realize that Berto might say 'No,' but you know how I operate. I'll explain it so Berto understands what's happening. Maybe I'll bend a few facts, but he'll go with me and it'll all work out. We girls always have a way with boys. You know that," Susan added confidently, "so don't worry about Berto. I can wrap him around my finger if I want. He seems so **tractable** and **obliging**; I think it'll be easy as apple pie."

Susan's words were so simple, so direct that I knew she'd have no problem asking Berto. However, a **pang** of jealousy **fomented** from within my **bosom**, as I realized I was **relinquishing** to her an **opportune** occasion to **inveigle** Berto into **chaperoning** her for the evening. My hesitation alerted her, and she quickly added, "But he's your problem after the prom, okay Janet?"

Those words **mollified** my **unfounded** and **jaundiced enmity**. "Thanks, Susan, you're a true friend," I added, deservedly **abashed**.

Susan and I had been close ever since the third grade but grew closer still when her mom passed away two summers ago. The **matriarch's untimely** death left the dad and her alone to care for two younger sisters and one baby brother. I contributed my part by helping watch over the baby and then meeting the two school-aged **siblings** after summer school to accompany them home. My efforts further **cultivated** an **esprit de corps** that **transformed** us from dear friends into **kindred spirits** and sisterly soul mates.

Susan's role as chief caretaker actually began several months earlier when her mom first became ill, responsibilities that included maintenance of the house and preparation of the meals. During those rare moments of **repose**, we would chat about my affairs with Tony and discuss my fears and uncertainties, but Susan **refrained** from discussing her own **pressing** concerns or suggesting how **onerous** her life had become. She remained a symbol of **indefatigable** strength and determination, and as times got tougher she got stronger. She **abstained** from alcohol but found **solace** in life's minor miracles, such as in the indestructible, **integral** soundness of the family unit and the inseparable bond of friendship that we shared. She was a **beacon** of hope and confidence who **excelled** in making others feel good – especially about themselves.

Susan possessed a rare **trait**, a **magnanimity** that shone brightly through the storms of **adversity**, and as we walked to the cafeteria I felt ashamed of my **petty** jealousy. Perhaps it would be fitting if she did find a nice boyfriend like Berto. No one deserved such happiness more than Susan, yet I knew she would never try to interfere with or compromise the happiness of her friends. Her own interests came second. She was truly a uniquely **compassionate** human being, a person I could only in my wildest dreams hope to one day **emulate**.

# CHAPTER XII
## *Turning It Around*

I feel a whole lot better now. It's been a long week, but I've come a long way. I think everyone in school has been talking about me, about how I tried to etch something in the desk during a history exam. I don't know what came over me. I seemed to be freaking out, like I was losing control over my life. But things are now looking up. The weekend in Maui helped **immensely**. My folks sure picked a good time to take a short vacation. I got the chance to clear my head, and I haven't dipped or chewed since Friday. That's almost one week without any tobacco, and it only took a couple of days to get over the withdrawal.

It's so easy to get hooked on cigarettes and tobacco. I used to tell people that it's just a small habit anyone can break, but when I tried to break it before, I always had one reason or another why I really didn't need to stop: I liked the taste, it made me feel warm, it made me look grown-up. I gave every reason I could imagine except one: I couldn't stop because I was hooked on it. The rest were merely excuses. I had simply gotten addicted to it. And this past week, I think I found just what it's like to kick the habit. It's like living in a **veritable** hell, like trying not to eat while you're in a lunch room. There's a hunger inside that **conjures** up every excuse possible to get you to just try one, just one small puff, or just to hold a cigarette between your fingers. Anything to get the tobacco closer to your mouth.

I know that my dipping and chewing and smoking have been **deleterious** to my health. I've heard enough stories about how a person as young as me is doubly affected by tobacco, how I'm like a balloon that hasn't yet been inflated – that every mark on my young body will be blown up in size with age, just as a small mark on a balloon grows as the balloon expands. I also think I've been smoking to punish my own body for all the things I've been doing to mess up my life. It's like taking a razor blade and cutting your skin all over just so you can see it bleed and feel it itch; it's the feeling that things are so screwed up, it doesn't matter if it gets worse; it's like shaving your head so everyone else can laugh at you. Kind of like an early form of self-destruction. And it all comes down to one reason, one simple reason: you feel that no one else cares. And after a while, *you* don't even care. Everything becomes pointless; there's no direction and no purpose. Life becomes just one long **bootless** journey of **despair**.

I didn't stop dipping because of the weekend trip to Maui. And it had nothing to do with Janet asking me today to go to the prom with her. It happened last week, right after class. It was a weird thing, and it **impelled** me to look more **introspectively** and analytically at myself and reconsider which path I should **ply** if I wished to **redeem** a life of **wayward wantonness** and **desultory dissipation**.

I've honestly never liked Mrs. A.'s class. She's a real **tyrant** who has always tried to **manipulate** us. Somehow, teachers perceive their role as that of **foreman** and their students their **minions**. But if only she remembered how her classmates regarded such teachers when she was in school, she would realize that she's not fooling anyone with such **pretentious** power. I guess I always wanted to make her look foolish by calling her bluff, and maybe that's why I tried to cause that scene last week. It really wasn't a major thing. I'd been dipping all day and was getting kind of buzzed out, and then I had a run-in with Alex before class, something over my not having done anything special recently to make the Demons look good. Boy, it really messes a person's mind when he's trying to straighten himself out and then his friends **exhort** him to **essay** more **nefarious exploits**. It's like **whetting** a wino's thirst by suggesting that a drink would be a fitting **finale** to the day.

Yeah, I guess I am a 'wino,' but it's not wine that gets to me. It's tobacco, pills and everything else I can find. But I've been able to stay dry for a week, and the last time I did anything stupid was the day all the action happened.

Anyway, I was **querulously splenetic** when I got into class, and I guess I wanted to do something **singularly novel** to **manifest** my **exasperation** and make the class take notice. I think that's why I did it. But when I started carving out the words on the desk in front of me, I didn't seem to know what I was writing. It was as though someone else had taken over and was speaking for me. I got really scared, and then Mrs. A. caught wind of what I was doing. That's what I really wanted to do – get her attention. But once I started carving those letters, it was a different ball game. A voice inside was trying to tell me something, but I never discovered what it was.

I was really buzzed when Mrs. A. started yelling. I can't remember what I said or did, though I was certain that the **upshot** would be my **expulsion** from school for my **flagrant vandalism**. But then someone covered up my staged **fiasco**, and I was spared. There were only six or seven people in that part of the room, and two of them were Demons. I thought it was Alex who assumed the attention, but that wouldn't make sense, not after he had earlier asked *me* to **initiate** some new **deviltry** – not unless he wanted to turn the event into a full-blown mutiny.

When the bell rang, I was just as helplessly wasted as before. I had an urgent need to get out of the class and get quickly to the bathroom. My stomach was cramping up and I could feel the tobacco slowly coming up my throat. The **noxiously asphyxiating** sensation was unbearable, like being in a car that's filled with gas fumes. Every breath was becoming **excruciatingly** difficult, and the **acrid** taste in my mouth made me feel as though I was choking on burning rubber. I knew I had to get out fast or else I'd be lying on the floor, sick to my stomach.

I made it to the bathroom after what seemed a millennium, running in with my arms across my stomach and crouching on my knees in front of the bowl. My mind was dizzy, my stomach ripping apart, and I welcomed the next few moments in which I could **purge** myself of the **baneful** substances that had **infiltrated** my body, a cleansing **analogous** to an escape from the **torturous** and **tenebrous** depths of *Hades* into the **empyreal splendor** of fresh open fields. I could breathe again; the **writhing** pain from the cramps **abated** and my head felt almost normal. I'd finally forced all the **toxins** out, and I knew right then and there that it was time to stop the spiraling descent into the **abyss** of self-**annihilation** and get back to living, if it were still possible. I knew I'd have a rough road ahead, but anything would be better than finding myself throwing up again in the middle of school. Once was enough.

*A voice inside was trying to tell me something...*

I pulled myself together and washed my face, but as I prepared to exit the bathroom I heard some **scuffling**. I couldn't see who was involved, but I recognized one of the voices: It was Alex's.

"You always go around kicking chairs?" Alex asked the other person.

"Only when I feel like it," a softer voice replied.

"Maybe it makes you feel good, huh?" Alex said. "Maybe you want to be some kind of clown or something, huh?"

I could tell that Alex was referring to the incident with the desk; I **fervidly** wanted to see whom he was talking to. But the painful cramps hadn't fully **subsided**, so I **resigned** myself to simply resting my stomach against the sink and leaning my head toward the faucets, ready to heave out my insides for a second time at any moment. The pain and the poison were obviously still of **paramount** concern.

"What's your beef about it?" the other boy continued, more forcefully. His voice seemed vaguely familiar, but I couldn't make it out for sure. It seemed to be a bit rougher than the new kid's, but it wasn't anybody else's I could recognize.

Another person spoke. "Look, man, when you kick up a chair in a class, that's your problem. But when it **upstages** what Tony's been doing, that's our problem." The unidentified speaker was obviously Stewart, one of the other Demons in the class. He must have thought I was trying to cause the scene on purpose – which may have been so at first, but not so toward the end. The desk-incident saved my neck, though nobody else seemed to realize it.

"Okay," the other boy replied, "I had a reason for it, and maybe you ought to think about what happens to a student who tries to **deface** school property. Or didn't you think about it?" The words seemed to indicate that he had kicked the desk over on purpose, as a cover-up or maybe in competition.

"Hey, don't tell us what to do," Alex replied angrily. I suspected that he was ready for a fight.

"You guys didn't say anything in class," the other boy responded. "You know why? 'Cause you didn't know why I was doing it. 'Cause maybe you thought I had another reason. And I did." The Demons were silent as he continued. "I did it because I've been through that kind of crap, getting my butt bounced around like a bowling pin. Being stuck up against the wall and **berated** by a bunch of **browbeating bozos**." It sounded like he was referring to a line-up in jail. The others listened quietly as he continued. "And if you've never been spit on and stepped on, you don't know what it feels like. But I'll tell you, it's no picnic, and once you've been through it you don't want to go through it again – and you don't want to see someone else go through it in front of your face. And that's what was going to happen. So I kicked the desk, and I did it as much for me as for anyone else. You guys want to watch someone else 'fry,' do it when I'm not around."

*...the painful cramps hadn't fully subsided, so I resigned myself to simply resting my stomach against the sink...*

The scene was silent.  I tried to walk outside, but every move I made seemed to reawaken my cramps, so I remained content to just lean safely over the sink.  At least I wasn't totally missing the  excitement, even if I couldn't see what was happening.

"Where are you from?" Alex asked the mysterious stranger.

"I'm from a lot of places," he replied casually.  "But all that I give a hoot about is that I keep myself from getting screwed by anyone or from watching someone else get screwed.  That's my excuse.  I'll watch out for myself, and maybe Tony can learn to think next time before he jumps into a fire.  'Cause next time, I may not be around to put the flame out."

The words were so perfect for the occasion, as though he had seen it all before and had full control over everything that happened.  The Demons remained in silence, perhaps in a state of shock.

Stewart's words finally came out, almost in fragments, as if he didn't know whether he should be **chiding** the person or **supplicating** for **clemency**.  "Hey, I'm sorry," he resumed.  "I didn't mean to put you down.  We all got our reasons, and I catch where you're coming from...I mean, sorry, okay?  Really."

I didn't hear anything else.  Nothing more was said.  It was as though the small group **dissipated** into the outer **realm** of **obscurity**; even the other lad remained **mum**.  He must have nodded or something, but he didn't say anything further or **endeavor** to claim center stage with **haughty histrionics**.  He merely did what he did for his own reasons, explained himself, and that was it.  No glamour, no bows.

While everyone else left to **bask** in the open air and enjoy lunch, I remained behind to regain my **equilibrium**.  I walked out a few minutes later, grateful that nobody had come into the bathroom and had seen me looking like a defeated **gnome**.  The guy had saved my reputation, though he had also shown to me just how **waywardly misguided** I had become.  And the odd thing is that he apparently had already gone through it all before, so he knew what he was talking about.  He was giving me a **prescient** glimpse into what I was headed for if I didn't **sober up** soon.

I didn't survive the day in school.  Before lunch was through I was in the nurse's office, **queasy** and lying **supine** on the cot, my hands clenched tightly against my aching stomach.  My folks came to pick me up, and I blamed my condition on having skipped breakfast – it was sure better than revealing the true reason why I was sick.  I **vowed** to myself right then and there that I'd do everything possible to get myself straightened out rather than face what the other kid obviously  knew only too well.  He'd gone through some really tough times himself, though during class I thought **verily** that the incident was an attempt to **upstage** me.  Now I realize that he never tried to steal the show; he simply made a small distraction to **defuse** the potentially **volatile** situation, and now I knew why.

I wanted to ask Alex who the boy was, but I was out of school for the rest  of the afternoon and then went to Maui for the next five days.  In **hindsight**, perhaps it wouldn't have been too wise to tell him that I'd overheard the conversation, for then he'd have discovered where I was and what I was doing there.

I went to Maui for a variety of reasons, but mostly to **mull** over and reevaluate my future direction. And all the time there, I kept **cogitating** what I had **erroneously** thought earlier – that no one else really cared for me. But now I know I was mistaken. There are at least three people who care. Janet is one, for sure. That's why she asked me to go to the prom. And I also care about myself. That's why I said "Yes" to her when she asked me today, because I do give a damn about myself and my future.

And then there is that third person, the nameless **benefactor** who rescued me. I'm not really certain whether what he told Stewart was truly his **motive** for kicking over the desk, but whatever his reason he clearly and caringly convinced me that I needed to straighten myself out and turn my life around **forthwith**. His **rationale**, though somewhat **covert** and **conjectural**, **bespoke** a **tacit manifestation** of **compassion** and **commiseration**. His actions reflected true concern, and for the first time in my **callow** life I **comprehended** that there are other people besides myself who are **impacted** by what I do. Maybe it took something like this to make me see that. Maybe now I can discover who I am and what I really want to be. I thought about that in Maui, and when I came back to school yesterday I knew it was time to look at everything in a different light. It was time to stop playing the **marionette** and start shifting for myself; and if I didn't listen to my parents or friends like Janet, then it was time to at least start listening to that voice inside me. Those words on the desk were trying to tell me something. And now I think I know what they were trying to say. I think I've discovered who I want to be. I do feel a whole lot better now.

# CHAPTER XIII
## *An "Old Friend"*

Tonight's the prom, but it's not going to be quite as I expected. I'm going with a girl named Susan McCarthy. It's kind of a long story about how I asked her. In fact, I think she asked me.

When I saw Janet on Monday, she was somewhat **standoffish**. I chatted with her briefly before history class, but I could sense that things weren't really right. I knew I was in for some bad news. "Hi Janet," I greeted enthusiastically as we both headed for class. "How was your weekend?"

She stared up at me in a **mystified** manner and answered, "Okay, I guess."

"You look kind of busy, like you're looking for something."

"Oh yeah," she said hesitating. "I lost...uh...something..."

She never **elaborated** but yet seemed absorbed in thought. I **opted** to reconfirm our upcoming date. "That Christmas prom is sure gonna be fun. I heard that *Music Express* will be putting on a wild light show."

"Oh, I didn't know that," Janet replied assuming an **aloof posture**. I could tell that she wanted to get to class. I'm not even sure she heard what I was saying.

Little was said after that. Class was boring, as usual. I was relieved, however, that Tony wasn't in school to do his cutting routine on the school desks, though also a bit concerned as to why he had gone **haywire** last week. I was equally concerned about Janet's faraway mood. Did I do or say anything to offend her? Did she know I was the one who kicked the desk? Did she hate me for it? I **resolved** to pursue the matter further as soon as class was over.

"Janet," I asked as she **scurried** out to lunch, "can we talk for a moment?"

"Sure, Berto," she replied politely.

I felt relieved that she was willing to listen to me. She seemed a bit less restless, yet still **preoccupied** over something.

"Are we still going to the prom together?" I was direct, but that's the way I am. I just don't believe in **mincing** words. If you want to ask something, ask it. That's my philosophy. You might as well get it out. The sooner, the better.

Janet's reply wasn't quite so direct. "I don't know, Berto. I'd like to, but something's come up and I'm really not sure."

*"I'd like to, but something's come up and I'm really not sure."*

The reply was the same as "No," except that she was leaving the door open for me to establish why the answer was "No."

"Is it something I did?" I asked as **concisely** and **explicitly** as possible. I didn't want to have **lingering** doubts or suspicions. If it was because of me, I needed to know.

"No, Shiloh," she replied softly, smiling as she spoke my nickname. I knew then and there that I was not the cause of her change of heart. Something else was bothering her.

"Are you planning to go with someone else?" I wanted to be **frank** but I could feel that this last inquiry was a bit too **prying**, that I was asking too much of her at this moment.

When Janet didn't answer, my doubts and suspicions resurfaced. I sensed that I wasn't going to find out anymore; I also realized that I'd need to make new plans if I wanted to go to the dance.

Another problem arose as well. Having given Janet a ring, was I still her 'steady'? And if so, did that mean I couldn't accompany another person to the prom? Worse yet, was our romance over? I had no clue, and rather than force the issue any further I just backed off and hoped we'd be able to continue tomorrow where we left off today, perhaps finding **resolution** to my **problematic quandary**.

I didn't sleep well at all that night. There's something about not knowing an answer that can drive a person crazy. It was like that day, a year ago in Owry, when I received a note in class that read "You're gonna get it," source and cause unknown. I didn't know when, where or by whom I would 'get it,' and I remember being ready at any given moment for battle. My **paranoia** spiraled out of control and exploded when I was tapped on the shoulder at lunch. I swung my body around and landed a solid right punch into my little brother's face, knocking him to the ground.

My first reaction was "So you're the guy who wrote that note," then **checked** myself and realized he had nothing to do with the note. He wasn't even in my class.

From that experience I learned that such notes are meant to **unnerve** and **cow** a person into **humble submission**. There's no action in such notes, only **veiled** threats. I'd have given anything to find out who had **masterminded** the **insidious** and **invasive intrigue**. I never did discover the person's true identity, but I did learn how to **cope** with such situations. As a result I became a stronger, more **self-reliant** individual who treated everyone else as though they had written the note. The note became a symbol of life itself: a warning that problems surface and **proliferate** when you least expect them to, that the only way to overcome such obstacles is to be constantly prepared beforehand. I became the **consummate vigilant** warrior, alert in both body and spirit. I had learned how to handle uncertainty.

Janet was more **vivacious** the following day. She approached me before school and in fact had been waiting for me to arrive on campus.

"Berto," she called in a **sprightly** and **vivified** manner as I got off the bus, "can I speak with you?"

"Sure, Janet," I replied wholeheartedly.

"Can you do me a favor?" she asked as she put her arms around my shoulders and stared **squarely** into my eyes.

I felt awkwardly uncomfortable. She was so direct, so **forward**; I wasn't sure what she would ask. If it weren't so early in the morning I might have considered the possibilities, but my brain was still in a **somnolent** state, so I simply waited for her to reveal what was on her mind.

"Would you mind if I went to the prom with someone else?" She came right out and asked the question boldly, squeezing me tightly as if to show that she still cared for me. She paused briefly and then continued. "It's with an old friend, that's all."

I **envisioned** her going to the prom with her dad or another older man, but then I realized what she meant by "old friend." My brain was slowly waking up – but I still had no idea who the other boy could be or whether it was really important for me to know, anyway. Maybe he was indeed just a 'friend' and I her 'steady boyfriend,' or maybe there was more to the story than I would ever know. I had no choice but to grant her my approval, though I now had no one to go with. I felt **rebuffed** and somewhat **ostracized**.

"But don't worry, Berto," Janet added, breaking the short silence, "'cause I've got a friend who wants to go, and yet nobody's asked her. Do you think you'd like to go with her?"

The question was too direct, too **abrasively curt**. My pride forced me to avoid saying "Yes" right away, even though I really wanted to go to the prom – especially if Janet would be there.

"Also, Berto," Janet continued in a more **deliberate** and cautious delivery, "there's another thing. I'm not 100% certain that I'll be going. It all depends if my old friend can make it."

"What if he can't make it, though?" I asked hopefully. "Maybe then we can go?" The question was reasonable, but I anticipated her reply.

"No, I think I'll just stay home in that case." She released her hold on my shoulders. "No offense, though, huh?"

"No, I understand," I said confusedly. I was utterly **nonplussed**. I'd been prepared for almost anything since my experience with the note, but at that moment I couldn't figure out where I stood. I was being shaken from my very foundation, and it could only happen at the hands of the 'weaker sex.' How **ironic**!

On Friday I found out that Janet was indeed going to the prom. And it was on that same day Susan asked me to go. I wanted to ask her myself, but even though I had suspected she was the girl Janet was referring to, my pride continued to **stifle** my courage.

"Hi Berto," Susan greeted as I was munching on a **palatable** teriyaki sandwich during lunch. "You remember me?"

"Sure, you're Janet's friend," I replied **congenially**. "The one last chance I have to go to the prom." My **uncensored** words came out too quickly and I could feel the sting of my unintended insult.

"Thanks for acting just like all the other boys," Susan responded, **rankled** by my insensitivity.

"Sorry, Susan," I apologized **abashedly**, my head bowed down.

"I accept. Now how about the prom? Are you going?" Her **undaunted** reply caught me off guard.

"Sure, if you'll have me." I wanted so desperately to go, nothing could **stanch** the **effusion** of my **effervescence**.

"Then we're going, you and me." she pronounced conclusively. "A couple of oddballs. Perfect for the evening."

Susan's good humor and **resilience** to my rude **initial** impression reflected her sunny **disposition**, a positive attitude that must have come from a lifetime without **hardship**. I admired her spirit and **joviality**. We became immediate **compatriots**.

Susan and I had lunch together that afternoon. As we **conversed** I asked about Janet and her 'old friend,' but Susan wouldn't yield anything concrete. "I'll explain it to you later," she kept repeating – but "later" never came, and I soon realized I would **ascertain** the true nature of events at the prom itself. I wasn't being given any sneak previews.

"Did I turn her off?" I asked **bluntly** as we walked to our next classes.

"No, that's not it. Janet's just gone through some tough times with an old friend. And now she's trying to help make things better."

"Does she love him?" I asked, my voice lower to sound more adult – but coming off like a **precocious** lad trying to sound mature.

"Jealous?" Susan asked **candidly**, sensing the source of my interest.

"No...yeah... a little, I guess." I simply couldn't deny the truth.

*I asked about Janet and her 'old friend,' but Susan wouldn't yield anything concrete.*

"Well then, Berto, we'll just have to go there to find out what it's really all about, yeah?" She had **piqued** my interest, and I knew then that the **multitude** of **misgivings** that had **muddled** my **mundane ruminations** would be **conclusively resolved** at the **momentous** event, with or without my presence.

"Is she going with Tony?" I asked with **bated breath**, exposing my suspicions. Janet had been unusually tense and **distractible** until Thursday, when Tony returned to school from what was apparently a vacation. He appeared relaxed and in greater control of himself, and Janet suddenly became **revitalized** and **rejuvenated** from the first moment she saw him. I wanted to chat with her at the time but she seemed determined to talk with Tony. During class the two were eyeing one another curiously, and it was then that I suspected a change in their feelings for one another.

"Does she love him?" I added before Susan could decide how to answer my earlier question.

"She feels sorry for him, Berto," Susan answered slowly and **somberly**. The humor was no longer **evident**, and I realized just how much Susan was trying to help Janet and her 'old friend.'

"Just tell me what you want me to do, okay?" I said in an **empathetic** and concerned tone. "Okay?"

"Thanks, Berto," Susan whispered with a smile. "And by the way, you're not like all the other boys. You're a very special boy, and I really appreciate the way you care. I really do."

For a moment I wished Susan, rather than Janet, was wearing my ring. But as quickly as I **entertained** that **notion** I **pondered** what it would be like having two girlfriends – each one unique in her own special way – in my life. My heart began to race as I **deliberated** the possibilities. The answers would all be spelled out at the prom.

I saw Janet once yesterday afternoon, and though I tried to avoid speaking with her and putting her on the spot, she ran over and began speaking to me. Her spirits were high and I could tell she wasn't about to tell me any of her problems – she didn't seem to have any.

"Berto, can I have a moment with you?"

I felt a bit silly. Why shouldn't I want to speak with my girlfriend. I thought about answering "No, I don't talk to people anymore" but I didn't want to risk injecting a scrap of **sophomoric** humor at this meaningful moment. Every word spoken between us represented precious, limited opportunities for sincere communication, and jokes were just not appropriate for the occasion. "Sure, Janet. Glad to see you're feeling so good."

"Thanks, Shiloh, you're so sweet." She then held my hand as she continued her thoughts. "I really appreciate your going with Susan to the prom. You really took the pressure off me."

I understood her reference to the 'pressure'; she could now go to the prom with her 'old friend' without feeling guilty leaving me unescorted.

"No problem, Janet. In fact, I think Susan's a super girl." The words came out both to inform and to produce a **pang** of jealousy. I knew I was being thoughtless and a bit cruel, but I needed to discover whether she still had **amorous** intentions for me. I waited eagerly for her reply.

Janet was visibly hurt by my comment, and I felt uncomfortably ashamed at my insensitivity. I'd never before thought very much how other people could be affected by my **callous** comments. In Owry, no one really cared what anyone else had to say; there is little room for **compassion** in a place where the sun never shines.

Here in Hawaii, though, everything seems so different. The sun shines every day and the island's inhabitants reflect a **radiant** sensitivity. And this caring is contagious, for I never before helped another person as I tried to help Tony. Sure, I helped Jake, but he's family and that's different. But in Hawaii it's like everyone is family; everyone cares about how others are **faring** and how they can **oblige** others' concerns.

Anyway, after **slighting** Janet with my heartless Owry-style comment I knew I needed to apologize quickly. I had no reason to want to hurt her. "Janet, I didn't mean to make it sound like I really want to take Susan out." But that didn't sound right, either. Everything I **strove** to say made less and less sense. I'd become very capable of handling my own situations with **aplomb** when involving other guys, whether back at Owry or here in Hawaii, but my relationship with girls was completely **confounding**. I needed to be more sensitive and more aware. Fortunately, Janet helped me out this time.

"Berto, don't worry about it. I know what you mean." She then explained the situation in finer detail. "You see, I really do like you, Berto. And I want to go steady with you. It's just that I've got to try to figure out how to help someone."

"It's Tony, right?" I asked **solemnly** and **earnestly**.

"It's just a friend, Shiloh," Janet answered, clasping my hand tightly. "Remember, he's just a friend."

Janet seemed almost on the **verge** of tears. I couldn't tell what was causing her to be so torn apart but could sense that her words to me were shared with complete **candor**. Every word she said was on the level; she really did like me a lot and nothing would change her feelings. We were still going steady, and any doubts I felt were now totally **unwarranted**. As we parted company that afternoon I felt confident that things might return back to where they were when we first exchanged our pledges of love. But I wasn't absolutely convinced; I had been in enough changing worlds to know that nothing lasts forever, that there is no such thing as security and predictability.

I've learned that the only thing in the world that doesn't change is a person's attitude. A **rational** person will always react consistently to **precariously vacillating** circumstances, adjusting appropriately when necessary; whereas, to an **addled** individual nothing will ever make sense. It all starts from within the person, and it all ends with him. The world isn't consistent; only the individual is. So when I learned my lesson from the anonymous note and from the weekend in Owry Juvenile Facility, I got myself on the right track so that I could be consistent no matter what **muddling** events might **transpire** down the road. But I never **deluded** myself into believing that life would ever become **pellucidly** predictable or **facilely traversable**. I only knew that I would be able to **contend** with life's **vicissitudes** with a sufficient **modicum** of success. I wasn't afraid when I came to Hawaii. I wasn't afraid when I had a showdown with a few of the Demons after the desk-incident on Friday, and I've learned not to ever let a situation take me off my guard. Even in the midst of a **maelstrom** I know I can **weather** the **turbulent** storm and keep myself in the **catbird seat**.

And I'm in a 'situation' now. The prom is tonight, Janet and her 'old friend' are going to be there, and yet I don't know if I'm really in love with Janet or Susan or anybody. The changes this week have been so sudden, unforeseen and emotionally draining that I wonder why I even bother to try to make friends. Sometimes it's easier just to remain alone.

But there's so much excitement in a life of change. I guess I wouldn't miss it for the world. Hawaii's not such a bad place after all, and not boring – that's for sure. I guess it's all up to the individual. I said that already, didn't I. Yeah, I guess I am really looking forward to the prom. With Susan, with Janet, and with whatever happens there. My stay in Hawaii has been filled with challenge, and having come so far I think I'm ready to handle some more excitement.

# CHAPTER XIV
## *Going With Tony*

I'm not sure I can stand the wait. Tony should be here any minute now. He told me yesterday that he'd meet me at my house so we can walk to the prom together. I live much closer to the school than Tony, but even so it's still a fifteen-minute walk. I was really surprised and excited when he said he wanted to walk with me to the prom. Actually, I was more surprised that he said "Yes" when I first asked him to go. I wasn't even sure I'd see him before the prom; he was out of school until Thursday.

When Tony walked into Mrs. Amagone's class, heads turned. **Devoid** of his former **disheveled** appearance, he was now dressed in a new pair of faded *501 Blues*, a white *Playboy* pullover and matching *Hound Dog* shoes. He bore the **semblance** of a **luminary, diametrically** different from the way he looked in the **dingy**, torn trousers and cutoff tee shirt he wore the prior week. He really looked **chic**, and as he sat at his desk he looked as though he were seriously interested in learning something. He really had changed. I couldn't believe my eyes.

"So you decided to show up finally," Mrs. Amagone **bellowed** out in her characteristically **condescending** manner. "You think you can learn something today, Renaldo?" The words were meant to **debase** and **dispirit**. She had such a poor sense of timing. Some of the other students **sneered** at the teacher's comments, and I could see Tony begin to slouch **dolefully** in his chair.

Fortunately, Tony maintained his composure – but I really lost my affection for Mrs. Amagone. She had always told us that she cared for us, no matter what we thought. But that **despicably** mean-spirited **indignity** targeting Tony was as far from sympathetic as I could conceive. Perhaps she had been teaching for so long that she'd forgotten how to relate to adolescents in an understanding manner. Especially to her own pupils, and especially to Tony.

I'll never understand why some teachers think students are **vacuous buffoons**. Last week, Mr. Garrett gave us some **convolutedly circuitous** directions for a reading assignment. Little Corey Tom raised his hand and asked **timidly**, "Could you repeat that again, please?"

Mr. Garrett made Corey a **laughingstock**. "What are those two things on the side of your head? Are they your nose? Your eyes? How about your ears? And what do ears do? Do they smell?" The class began to chuckle and **snicker**. Mr. Garrett had raised the possibility that Corey's ears smelled. He continued with **derisive** delight. "Do they see? Do they hear? And how can they hear unless you listen? And what do you need to do when you listen? You need to think. And thinking requires a brain. So when you don't hear a word I'm saying, you're telling everyone here that you don't have a brain. So I'll ask you one time, did you understand the directions?"

Corey was on the spot. He had no choice but to say "Yes" even though he had probably lost his concentration midway through the **despot's dehumanizing disparagement**.

"Good, Mr. Tom. I'm glad you know the complete directions. Now for the sake of all of us who need to be informed, I'd like for you to come up here to the front of the class and **enlighten** us to the directions."

Mr. Garrett was **intent** on making Corey a **martyr** to prove a meaningless point: that he was able to twist Corey's innocent request into a confession of stupidity. The **diffident** boy sat frozen, then burst into tears as he put his head on the desk.

"My oh my," Mr. Garrett continued victoriously, "is this the way a teenager should behave?" Corey was totally **demoralized**. The teacher's **subjugating** torture was complete.

But Tony didn't crack like Corey did. He simply slouched at his desk and rode out the storm. He was determined to survive against any **degradation** Mrs. A. could deliver. He was indeed a **markedly** changed person.

I called out to him after class, eager to talk with him about the prom. Tony reacted with **ebullience** upon seeing me, and I knew a long-overdue **metamorphosis** had **eventuated** since I last saw him in school the week before. "Hi Janet," he sparkled. "Gosh, it's nice to see you."

"Gee, Tony, you sure look cool," I remarked **exuberantly**. "Where were you during the week? I heard you left the island. I really missed you." My **intimate** and **uninhibited** questioning reawakened a **kinship** with my long-lost **sibling**. It was the first time in months that we were exchanging heartfelt words, and my body hungered to return to the **halcyon** days of *steal away* and youthful innocence.

"I went to Maui," Tony replied openly. "Just a short trip to a neighbor island, that's all. But it sure felt good."

"You sure look good," I re-emphasized with a girlishly **giddy** giggle. "I'm really sorry about the way I've been acting," I added, hoping to **elicit** some **overt** and **palpable** reaction from him.

"No, don't apologize," he answered **meekly**. "I'm the one who's been screwing up. I don't know what came over me. I just got into some bad habits and started listening to the wrong people, that's all. But that wasn't your fault. I'm glad you still care about what I'm doing. I'm the one who should be apologizing."

His words were delivered so **deferentially** and sincerely that I was speechless. Tony seemed to have discovered some secret for self-correction, and I didn't know how to respond. If he'd have come back as a reborn Christian, that would have made more sense. But his **conversion** was merely the product of a **transformational** rather than **metaphysical epiphany**. He simply reevaluated his position and charted a new course.

*I knew a long-overdue metamorphosis had eventuated since I last saw him in school the week before.*

"Tony, would you like to go to the prom tomorrow? I would've asked you sooner but you were gone all week." I didn't want to say that I had no serious intention of asking him earlier – when he was acting **testy** and **irascible** — but Tony knew what I was thinking.

"Yeah, I know," he added calmly, "and I was 'gone' before that, too. Really freaked out, for sure. You know that, I know that. But I'm sure glad you feel like asking me now. You're about all I've really got..." He paused as if wishing to say more but unable to phrase it to his satisfaction. Instead, he simply **peered** searchingly into my eyes and waited. He had found who his true friends were and was now making **amends** with them. Perhaps he had **reconciled** his differences with his family on Maui, or perhaps he had simply found peace within himself. Obviously, he had done a lot of soul-searching during the week and found what he was looking for. "I'd love to go," Tony concluded. "But I thought you'd be inviting that new kid."

"No, Tony, I didn't plan to. Well, maybe I was thinking about it, but then I realized you're the one I want to go with." I bit my lip as I said the last few words. I had fallen in love with Berto too, and now it hurt twice as much to tell Tony that I really didn't want to go with Berto.

Why is it that whenever you get a boyfriend, you've suddenly got two? And when you haven't got any, there's nothing you can do to get one? That seems one of the **ironies** of life. That old **cliché** really is true: "When it rains, it pours." And there I was, in the middle of a rainstorm trying to decide whom I loved more, when I knew all the while that love doesn't come in degrees. It's either there or it isn't there. And when it's in two places, there's nothing you can do but accept both and hope you don't drown in the **deluge** – or worse yet, that the two don't destroy each other in **mortal** combat. The tales of *Guinevere* and *Sir Lancelot* were great as romance stories, but there's nothing glamorous about having two wonderful people fight one another over you. Either way, you lose.

I remember watching *The Little Rascals* a few weeks ago and thinking of Tony and Berto as being *Butch* and *Alfafa* – and I as their *Darla*, their *Snow White*. *The Little Rascals* was only a **juvenile** television program, but as I sat **entranced** I envied *Darla* and how the boys would fight for her love. But now I see that she wasn't in love with either of them. She only wanted to have herself placed on a pedestal from which she could **flaunt** her **celebrity** and **revel** in **sycophantic** adulation. Maybe she had a "*Shirley Temple* complex" after all, on and perhaps even off the screen.

I didn't want to have Tony and Berto at odds with one another, but neither did I want to mislead Tony into believing that Berto meant nothing to me. And I certainly didn't want Berto to get that idea. I felt terribly confused speaking in riddles to Tony, but I feared telling him any more. I thought he might once again **unravel**, and I knew I'd never forgive myself if I **vitiated** all his recent reforms with a well-intentioned **veracious** appraisal that might actually **sabotage** all the personal **strides** he had recently achieved.

Tony and I discussed plans for going to the prom. I was content simply to meet him at the school, but he asked if he could come to my house and then accompany me personally to the event.

I agreed wholeheartedly with his request, feeling the thrill of anticipation imagining myself hand-in-hand walking with the boy I never thought I'd be with ever again.

I saw Berto after school and we shared a brief but **frank** conversation. But I hesitated in telling him everything about Tony, although I feel he suspected. I could even sense a slight **twinge** of jealousy by the way he **rationalized** that he was beginning to like Susan. I could feel an insecurity **welling** up within him, and I felt both proud and ashamed to have forced him to defend himself while desperately **vying** for my affection.

I know Berto cares for me, and now I'm being torn between two boys. The prom is going to be very unpredictable, to say the least. I don't know what's going to happen when Berto sees Tony, but I do know I won't have any control over the matter. The simple fact is I'm in love with two boys, though I guess Tony's still my first choice. And there I go again, making choices. It isn't fair. Someone's going to get hurt. Either Berto, Tony, or me. Or maybe all of us. I know I've got to be very careful with what I say and do at the prom, but though I'll be walking directly into the lion's den I'll be walking proudly side-by-side with Tony. I sure hope Berto will also be on our side. Gee, I don't know what I'll do if anything goes wrong. Oh, I hope nothing goes wrong.

## CHAPTER XV
### *Picking Up The Pieces*

Janet's waiting for me, but I can't seem to figure out the right words to say when I see her. I bought a beautiful purple **corsage**, but what do I say to her when I step off the bus? I thought I had **resolved** all my issues but now I'm totally **flustered** – I've got butterflies in my stomach. I've never felt like this before – not about Janet, not about anyone else in my life. I can't tell if it's love or stage fright or both, but I really hope the bus stops at every corner. I need more time to think.

I sure knew the words to say when I told Alex and Barry that I wasn't going to be the Demon leader after this year: that I had a girlfriend to worry about instead. At first they looked **askance** at me – eyeing me **dubiously** and **incredulously** – but when I **apprised** them of my **reconciliation** with Janet they **curbed** their **captious** and **caustic castigation** and instead bit the bullet with reluctant **reticence**. After all, I wasn't **defecting** to another club; I was simply assuming a more mature role and pursuing a more purposeful path. I could never have gotten away with such **dialectic justification** when I was younger, but it proved effective last night and I was able to **extricate** myself from the one remaining obstacle in my social life. I could now spend my time constructively focused on Janet rather than destructively on gang activities.

I really had a marvelous time in Maui, and I never once had the desire to **filch** or **defile** anything, paint my name on a wall or try to pick a fight with anyone. Instead I enjoyed lying on the beach and just thinking about life in general. And about Janet. And about myself. Mostly about myself. And I became **enlightened** to one **immutable** fact: I am the only person in my life who can listen to me. If you can't listen to yourself – if you can't talk to yourself and get out your thoughts – then you've got nobody. That guy was right last week when he said you've got to stand up for yourself. It made sense to me when I heard it, and it made even more sense when I had time to dwell on it at length on Maui. I needed to listen to myself – listen to the words carved on the desk, the words that came from deep inside. Maybe those were the first signs that I had something to say, something different from what everyone else had **ascribed** to my **ignominious nonentity**. During my brief **sojourn** to the adjacent island, this new realization slowly began to sink in, from the words the mysterious stranger had said to my own reflection on the whole **revelatory** incident.

I realize just how fortunate I was in avoiding being hauled over the coals at the hands of Mrs. A. and in not **regurgitating** my tobacco breakfast if I were **compelled** to speak in my own defense; I'd have been shamed for the rest of my miserable life at that school. I can just imagine what everyone would have said about me: I'd have been known as the school junkie, the nicotine king or whatever other unflattering **epithets** they'd have attached to **disparage**, **excoriate** and **vilify** me.

I came back from Maui fully appreciative of my inner feelings, of my need to express myself and not follow somebody else's **injudicious** advice. Quitting the Demons was a decisive and daring determination, and I did it because I wanted to, not because someone else urged me to. Going with Janet to the prom has also been my own personal decision governed by a desire to travel upon that **proverbial** straight and narrow path. And I'm so happy about that. I feel an inner strength knowing I've been able to recover what I feared was slipping away during my period of moral decline. I was starting to lose everything, but in one week much of it returned to me. Especially Janet.

But I've still got butterflies in my stomach. Maybe it's because I'm now moving in an **auspicious** direction for the first time in many months and have reestablished a positive **rapport** with someone I **cherish** dearly.  Or perhaps it's a mixture of **apprehensiveness** and **angst** arising from the **inconstant** and **mercurial** nature of my relationship with Janet.

I need to pay close attention to what Janet says and does at the prom, just in case I've **misconstrued** her sentiments.  I know she's been seeing Berto, but I don't believe she's been using him as a vehicle of revenge; I believe she genuinely cares for him.  And I also can't help but suspect that he was the boy who faced the Demons last week, though I really don't know that for sure, either. Come to think of it, maybe that's why I'm so excited – because I'm so overwhelmed.  It's an odd feeling indeed but one I am willing to face head on without **reservation**.  It's time I begin to stand up for myself – that's what the mysterious stranger said I should do.

The bus will be arriving in front of Janet's house in a few short minutes, but I feel more **self-assured** now.  I really wonder what it's like to be a new kid in town.  When Berto first started coming to Ocean View I wondered whether he felt like a complete **pariah**, an alien in a foreign land, or whether he was prepared to make the most of the new experience.  When I first saw him I suspected – and quietly feared – that he might be competition, but as time went on I found him to be a **placid** and **self-possessed** soul uninterested in **usurping** my leadership role.  Yet I also soon sensed that beneath his **serene** and **nondescript** exterior lay a **stealthy**, **puissant** animal capable of savagely pouncing on unsuspecting, **foolhardy** prey that dared **encroach** upon its personal **domain**.  It was just the way he acted – shy but not afraid.  I think Janet noticed him from the first day of history class.  I didn't.  But when I noticed Janet looking over at him, then I began to notice him  more and more, too.

He's an odd fellow, an **anomaly** of sorts: quiet and shy, and rather **incurious** regarding the affairs of his **peers**.  At first glance I thought he was a pushover, but as I observed him more closely I **descried** a bit of a hardness – or confidence perhaps – in his eyes that made me a little afraid of him.  I wouldn't have **conceded** that before.  In fact, I think I said to myself I wanted to beat him up.  But I don't think I was ever serious about it.  There was just something about him that told me I wasn't **privy** to the whole story.  And I wasn't **daredevil** enough to pursue the secrets he held.

I introduced myself to him two weeks after school **commenced**, but he hardly said anything.  I **endeavored** to continue the conversation the following day, before class began, and **availed** myself of the opportunity when I **espied** him leaning against a wall writing what appeared to be a letter.  As I approached him I could **discern** marks around his eyes, almost like premature **crows-feet**.  He didn't seem the least bit **disconcerted** as I **encroached** upon his personal space, as though he had no fear of anyone, as though he'd already passed successfully through the **stygian void** of the  **chthonian** underworld.  I felt a little envious – maybe even a little jealous – but yet something  inside cautioned me not to seek to penetrate his **esoteric** and **inviolate covenant** with darker forces  I could not in my most terrifying of nightmares have **conjured** up.

In height and weight Berto and I match up pretty evenly, but in a fight I'd lose in a minute.  I know I'd lose.  The real reason I'd become leader of the Demons was so I could avoid **confronting** anyone one on one.  I felt that the group would give me strength, but actually all I did was **cower** behind the others while pretending to be their leader.  And the more I tried to act the part of the **dreaded** Demon, the more **outlandish** I behaved.  I may no longer have been looked upon by others as a **recreant**, but instead I had **transformed** myself into what was perceived as a social misfit.  It was a lose-lose **transposition**.

I've discovered that you've got to take responsibility for your own actions, you've got to make up your mind who you really want to be and then follow that ideal. Nobody should ever be able to change who you want to become. I guess that's what made me secretly envious of Berto. Nobody could change him. Not me, not the Demons, not even the teachers. I guess Berto was somebody I really wanted to be like. As the weeks passed I grew to envy him more and more and myself less and less. But now I really don't find myself obsessed with Roberto Gonzalez. Instead I'm happy to be who I am, and that's all that should really matter.

I don't know if Janet's going to accept me back into her life again. She's been going with Berto for a while, I'm certain of it. I even heard she's wearing his ring. That may be true, but I've got one advantage over him: I've known Janet a lot longer, and if that means anything I may still be her Number One boyfriend. Nonetheless, I sure hate to compete with Berto. He has such confidence, such an **air** of experience about him that puts me on notice that I'm competing against the best.

I had one brief **encounter** recently with Berto. It happened a couple of weeks ago, when I was spiraling out of control. It was during the morning-recess period, when the Demons **congregated** to establish a **consensus** over which **puerile machinations** to **perpetrate** for the **forthcoming** week. George, Alex and Stewart had suggested **duping** a Waikiki tourist into purchasing a fake *Rolex* watch and then celebrating the financial **windfall** by **carousing** through the night, but with the vacation sites securely policed the idea didn't sound **prudent** or **feasible**. And since we were now older and physically more mature than when we were sixth or seventh graders, people would be naturally more suspicious of a group like ours, making it more difficult for us to get away with such **chicanery**.

Alex suggested painting our logo on one of the hotel walls, but no one else favored the idea. We'd been busted awhile back, caught **red-handed** while drawing a picture of a nude girl on the bathroom wall at *Waikiki Billiards*. We agreed to repaint both restrooms – men's and women's – and considered ourselves fortunate that the manager didn't **summon** the authorities and press charges against us.

During our **protracted** meeting Roberto was nearby, resting against a tree and reading a book. I called over to him for a bit of outside advice.

"Hey, chum," I said boldly, "what would you do to have a good time?"

Berto looked up **impassively** from his book, surveyed the scene and answered "Maybe go skateboarding."

The reply seemed so logical, natural and **apropos** for a group like ours. George and Alex looked **askew** at one another as if to say "What a dumb idea," though deep inside I think we all favored the suggestion. But we couldn't **concur** so **readily** with what an outsider had offered; it would have made our **collaboration** appear **ineffectual**.

"Thanks for the help, stranger," I answered **feigning** a **perfunctory** and **obligatory** response which masked my true appreciation for his **timely** advice.

Berto didn't reply, and as I looked up and stared at him he just went back to reading his book. I

*During our protracted meeting Roberto was nearby, resting against a tree...*

had certainly expected him to try to get closer to our **elite** group, having been personally addressed by me, their **exalted** leader.  But he expressed no interest, no deep secret desire to become one of us. I envied his independence and began to wonder why the Demons couldn't even decide on one thing to do, while Berto could do anything he wanted.  Why did my weekend **diversion** depend on what others preferred?  And why were our activities always destructive or daring?  What were we trying  to prove?

Yeah, that was my one short conversation with Berto.  We didn't say much, but much was learned.  He was free and **unencumbered**, whereas I was at the mercy of a pack of lost souls, going nowhere and headed there fast.

I remember one word from the conversation that really haunted me afterwards.  It was the word "stranger."  I had called Berto a "stranger" almost as though wishing for him to join us and become our "friend."  But as it turned out, I think *we* looked like the strangers, each of us looking rather odd in our own way.  Berto was the only person who truly knew what he was doing.  We were all hung up on unrealistic images of ourselves and our group, **quixotic** visions of **notoriety** that seemed to stop us from doing what we really wanted.  Berto might very well have gone skateboarding that weekend – and I would have been honored to join him – but our **discordant** group couldn't agree on anything, so I spent the weekend sitting at the park, dipping and spitting my future prospects into a paper cup.  *I* was becoming the stranger, stranger to the group, stranger to the world, stranger to myself.

I sure hope this bus doesn't continue to stop at every corner.  I've just got to see Janet.  I need to tell her how much I love her.  I need to let her know.  I don't want to be a stranger anymore.

## CHAPTER XVI
### *The Confrontation*

I never knew what a prom was really all about.  I thought it was just dinner and a dance.  But I learned something new last weekend:  I learned that a prom is about people – people like Janet, Tony, Susan… and myself – and that a prom is like life, a road where nothing follows a straight path. I came to Hawaii thinking I knew everything there was to know about life, but maybe I arrived with too much confidence. At the prom Tony set me straight; he showed me that you can never count your chickens before they hatch, even if you think you're sitting pretty on them.  The prom really  was an experience, an evening in which everything that could happen did happen.  Nobody was left out.  It was a an eye opener, an **apocalypse** of sorts, for all of us.

My mom drove me to pick up Susan and was naturally **inquisitive** whether I was going steady with her.

"No, mom, I'm going with Janet."

"But where's Janet?" she asked, **perplexed**.

"She's going to the prom with an 'old friend,'" I replied.

"An 'old friend' or a 'boyfriend'?" she questioned.

"Probably both," I responded openly.

"So you're taking out the runner-up, huh?"

"Well, not really.  Susan is Janet's best friend."

By now my mom was completely confused.  "So you're going with your girlfriend's best friend because she's going out with another boyfriend."  She hesitated for a moment, then added, "What kind of friends do you have, anyway?  In my day things like that just didn't happen.  You either went to the prom with your girlfriend or you didn't go at all."

"But Mom," I defended, "it's not like you think.  It's just that Janet has a long-time friend that she wanted to take.  I've only been in Hawaii for a few months."

"So that means you can go steady with a girl who already has a boyfriend?"  Her questions resembled the **stereotypical interrogation** from a Jewish mother.

"Mom," I repeated, "he's only a friend, not her boyfriend."

But my mom couldn't be convinced. "When two people go to a prom together, it means something. That's all I'm saying. And you are going to the prom with someone, aren't you?"

"You know I am, mom."

"Do you like her, Roberto?" she asked seriously.

"Yeah, I guess. But it's different with Susan."

"I don't see why. A prom is a prom is a prom. Just like a marriage is a marriage is a marriage."

I didn't appreciate her association of prom with marriage. I had already seen one marriage turn sour but I kept my personal remarks to myself. Jake had made enough **condemnatory** comments about the separation to speak for both of us; I didn't wish to contribute to the bitterness of the past.

"Mom, are you trying to tell me something?" I asked directly.

"Me? Why should I? It's your life. But I think you should be a little bit watchful, boy. You need to be careful **lest** you get burned. Best be watching where you're headed. Or maybe you'll be marrying the wrong girl."

I was **incensed** at the last remark. "I'm not marrying anyone, mom. I'm only going to a dance, a simple high school dance. And that's it. Pure and simple. Take it or leave it."

"For better or for worse," she added cleverly. She took the wind out of my sails.

"Okay mom, you're right. For better or for worse. I know what you mean." I hesitated and collected my thoughts before continuing. "Should I be going to the prom with Susan?" I asked indecisively.

"Yes, you should," she answered **assertively**. "But just don't try to use her to get you closer to that other girl. She's not worth 'using.'"

"Yes she is," I replied **viscerally**.

"No, honey. No girl is worth it. Get what I mean? No girl is worth 'using.'"

What she really meant was that no girl should be used for personal gain. I think her focus was on Susan, not Janet. She wasn't **reproving** Janet for having another boyfriend. She was blaming me, in a **subtle** motherly way, for trying to get to Janet by using Susan. I could sense her meaning, though it was very hard to put into simple words or respond to quickly and easily. I knew she was right, and she understood my silence.

"Just be careful, okay Roberto? You want to have a good time, so make sure you have one. But don't set your hopes on too much. Be happy with what you've got."

I guess mom had been happy with what she had. But dad wasn't. He wanted more, always pushing for a raise or else preventing another from getting one. For him life was one big competition match from which only one winner emerged. But in his **assiduous** attempt to reach the top he eventually discovered that no one ever wins in such **nebulous quests**. It's just a matter of time, but everyone **inevitably** loses. When he lost, it cost him more than just his job. It cost him his wife and children. He lost it all. And now my mom didn't want me to follow in his footsteps. She didn't want to see me risk everything for one **elusive** prize. "Be happy with what you've got" seemed most appropriate, and I **dwelt** on her **pithy aphorism** as we continued our ride to Susan's house.

Susan was waiting patiently outside, maturely attractive in a white frilled dress and high-heel shoes. As she approached the car, my mom greeted her as though she were part of the family, exchanging **cordial pleasantries**.

"Roberto has told me so much about you," my mom said as they hugged one another through the open window. I was sure that Susan thought my mom was mistaken – that I must have been talking about Janet – but she was nevertheless happy to be so warmly received. My mom was obviously trying to make a point, though I couldn't quite put my finger on what it was. Oddly, Susan seemed to understand, as though they had exchanged secret notes during the hug – as though females communicated through **recondite** means that us guys will never **fathom**.

I felt a little left out for the rest of the ride to Ocean View School. My mom and Susan were absorbed in all kinds of talk about one thing or another – especially about Susan, her family, her future plans, and other **mundane** and seemingly **banal** matters. Now I know why girls can talk over the phone for hours. They just keep **rambling** on and never really get anything said. Or if they do, its **abstruse import** is beyond my **ken**.

It was a few minutes past seven when we arrived at the edge of the campus. My mom gave Susan another of her mysteriously meaningful hugs, then Susan and I proceeded to the prom hand in hand. I can't even remember whose idea it was to be holding hands, but there we were, walking as though we were going steady. I felt a conflict of emotions – **uneasy** on one hand and yet secure in the other. Secure in the hand that held Susan.

Over a hundred couples had arrived before us and were **sauntering** about, **assimilating** the **blithe** and **convivial ambience** of the school that rarely appeared this pleasant and inviting. The campus was particularly **radiant** under the **shimmering** rays of the **lambent** Hawaiian moon. Although it was usually filled with a thousand students **bustling** from one class to another, today it looked as though it were designed for two hundred people, each pair of whom could stake out a small parcel of the campus to chat, **reminisce** and be as 'alone' as they desired. There was magic in the air, and loud-speakers in every hall **heralded** the **felicitous** occasion with the pre-recorded theme-song *Honolulu City Lights*:

> *"Each time Honolulu city lights stir up memories in me;*
> *Each time Honolulu city lights bring me back again."*

Susan and I sat on a bench near the school cafeteria, observing couples float by from all sides in **amorous** anticipation of the evening that lay ahead. Susan and I weren't so **rapt** in fantasy, directing our conversation instead to more **prosaically pragmatic** concerns.

"Have you seen Tony?" Susan whispered as I lay **recumbent**, looking up at the **glistening** stars.

"Well, I haven't seen Janet yet, but I think they'll show up soon."

Susan paused, confirming for me that Janet was indeed going to the prom with Tony. My initial reaction was mixed, but then I began to feel somewhat pleased and relieved knowing that Tony, the person I'd helped **avert** disaster and humiliation in Mrs. A.'s class, was being given another chance to reunite with Janet. If he had learned anything from the **didactic** experience, he'd have to demonstrate it for Janet tonight. This was truly the final exam testing his character.

For my part, if I wanted to help Tony pass the test I'd need to stay close to Susan and not act like a Honolulu version of Skip the gang leader. Tony had enough trouble keeping his head above water, and if my own selfish actions **undermined** his efforts and caused him to lose Janet, I'd never respect myself again.

When dad left mom, he left no forwarding address behind, no money for her, nothing. He simply ran away, and I said then I'd never forgive him for that. His own **ego** was worth more to him than his friends, wife or family were. By risking everything to protect his pride, he had lost his job. But when he left us behind without any interest in helping us, he lost a great deal more: he lost the faith and respect of his own family. I'd realized then and there that the worst thing a person can do is bail out of a ship in stormy seas, leaving everyone else to **perish**. It's the sign of true weakness. And were I to **undermine** Tony's efforts to **redeem** himself in Janet's eyes, I'd be as guilty as my dad neglecting his responsibilities to his family. For me, the neglect would be as a fellow human being, a person who should give a damn about how another person feels, especially since I'd been in his shoes myself before.

I really shouldn't act as though I've been abandoned in the midst of all the problems that have happened in my life; in fact, I've received **ample** guidance and assistance. From all the supportive counselors who tried to help me when I was getting into trouble in Owry, all the way to Janet – who helped me discover the magic of the islands – I've always found friends along the way. And my mom has always been around to help answer my questions and direct me with her wisdom and strength. Even now, Susan was with me at the prom to help keep me on the right track, to offer her companionship when I most needed someone to share this special evening with.

*"Have you seen Tony?" Susan whispered…*

I suddenly felt a strong sense of belonging come over me as I lay back and gazed once more at the stars, aware that Janet's happiness depended greatly on how I would react to her 'old friend.' I really wanted to contribute to making the prom an evening for her to treasure forever, even if I didn't figure in her ultimate plans. I owed it to Janet and I owed it to Tony. But I especially owed it to mom.

Susan and I spent most of the evening together, separating momentarily to **converse** with fellow students who passed by – mostly girls who were long-time friends of hers. A couple of my acquaintances attracted my attention briefly, but the majority of the friends we met were Susan's. Nevertheless, she stuck closely to me and we found ourselves quite comfortable in one another's company, avoiding the glitter and noise of the disco dance that was taking place in the main auditorium.

It wasn't until after nine o'clock that we first saw Tony and Janet. They had apparently arrived late; otherwise, we would have noticed them earlier. They were extremely **subdued** and **inhibited**, as though afraid or **wary** of something. It didn't take a genius to realize who they were watching out for. Susan cautioned me as we approached.

"Don't say anything, Berto. Let them do the talking. I don't know what they've been discussing, so please be careful, okay Berto?" Susan seemed especially concerned, as though a great deal lay on the line tonight. I had already established that fact, but her **admonition** made me more **chary** and **circumspect** about **interjecting** a **faux pas** that might **engender catastrophic** consequences. I needed to keep my personal comments to myself.

"Hi, Janet," Susan called out cheerfully, letting go of my hand in the process. "How's everything going with you?" She addressed herself only to Janet, pretending to ignore Tony's presence. She obviously didn't want to make a spectacle out of anything. I could see Tony slowly move behind Janet as though afraid I'd beat him up. I wanted to speak out, to say something to make him feel more at ease, but since Susan had better control of the situation I kept the words to myself.

"Things are really fine, Susan," Janet replied. She then addressed me in a **straightforward** manner, though I could tell she was trembling deep inside, fearing what I might say. "How is everything with you, Berto?"

I smiled politely back at her, avoiding Tony's worrisome looks. "I'm doing real well. It's a great prom, isn't it?"

Susan looked up at me in slight shock. She hadn't expected for me to be so gracious; she also realized that I meant every word. Janet also gazed at me **befuddled**. I was not trying to make her jealous, but my **unaffectedly jovial** reply did have a stinging effect on her.

"Gee, Berto," Janet replied courteously, yet understandably offended, "I'm glad you're having such a good time. I'm happy for both of you."

I wasn't expecting such a reply and didn't want to be misunderstood. I certainly didn't want Janet to think I didn't love her; that's the last thing I would have wanted her to believe. "Janet, let's just say that I'm having the second best time I could be having." The words carried the message well, but unfortunately everyone there understood what I meant. Janet and Susan. And Tony. There was no way I could rephrase the comment or tiptoe around the conflict. Both Tony and I had a crush on Janet, and no matter whose might be stronger, neither of us could deny our feelings.

My mom's advice flashed across my mind, but I couldn't follow it. "Sorry mom," I thought to myself, "there's only one girl in my life right now and that's the goal I've gotta go for, no matter what the cost." Maybe my dad had the same **compelling** motivational impulse to succeed when he tried so hard to advance himself; perhaps he did it for the good of the family, too. And maybe his loss wasn't **inevitable**; perhaps it was just a twist of fate. For the first time since the day he walked out, I began to feel that maybe he wasn't completely at fault; perhaps nobody was. Maybe that's just the way life is, filled with obstacles, some of which can't be avoided or overcome. Sometimes you've just got to take the chance and sail in stormy waters, even if you may have to one day bail out. You can't always stay on dry land.

I realized then that I was walking into a storm this evening, one involving me and Tony. If he were **hardy** enough, he would need to show it tonight in defense of his girlfriend. I wouldn't simply walk away from Janet and let her think I didn't care. Maybe it was my pride, or possibly my sense of honesty; but whatever the reason, I wouldn't allow myself to play the part of **hypocrite** and fool. I wanted Janet to know how I really felt, no matter how much it might hurt everyone. I was no longer interested in **dissembling** my true feelings. The time had come to **own up** to who I was and what I stood for.

Susan wrapped up our brief **encounter**, but I felt certain we'd be meeting again before the night was through. I still had a lot to say to Janet – and to Tony.

My evening with Susan took a decidedly negative turn. She soon discovered how I felt and that I intended to eventually **confront** Janet and Tony. Once I had made my feelings known, all that remained to be seen was where the night would take us. But between me and Susan, we were going nowhere. She was no longer my date but simply my dance companion, my ticket to get into the prom. Yet she took it very well, not staging any **histrionics** over my **overtly manifest** desire to pursue Janet or of my disinterest in developing a closer relationship with her.

The moment of **reckoning** came around 11:00 p.m. in the auditorium, site of the school dance. Susan **prompted** the action with words I had been waiting for all evening. "Berto, why don't you ask Janet to dance? She's not doing anything right now, and Tony's with some of his friends. Go for it. I'll wait here."

My thoughts began to race wildly, **curbed** behind a **cloak** of courtesy. "Are you sure?" I asked with **mannered solicitude**. I didn't wait for her reply.

90

The **opportune** moment had arrived, and I practically jumped off the seat and flew to Janet. "Would you like the next dance?" I asked as I rushed to her.

Janet seemed surprised, perhaps not so much that I was asking her for a dance but by the way I sprang to ask her, as though I were let off my chain and set free. "Sure, Berto" was all she said.

I had put Janet on the spot, and she didn't know how else to react. But she didn't say "No," so I knew she **longed** for this moment at least half as much as I did.

The dance was a slow one, much to my delight. We were close to one another and could whisper rather than yell our words.

"Having a good time?" I asked in gentlemanly fashion.

"Yeah, it's sure a nice prom," Janet replied politely.

"Do you love Tony?" I didn't want to waste time.

Janet looked at me somewhat startled, sensing my burning curiosity, and then answered **candidly**, "Yes, I think so."

The words hurt, but I felt **impelled** to persist with further questioning and hope the answers wouldn't be as similarly **devastating**: "Do you still love me?"

"Yes I do, Berto," she replied openly. "I love both of you."

I heaved a sign of relief; I had not become the loser. But I could not conceive of two winners when it came to the battle of love. The next **query** followed **spontaneously**. "Who do you love more, Janet?"

Janet paused. I think she had the answer – I feared she had the answer. But she held back and then responded slowly and **discreetly**, "You're both my friends. You're both special. You both mean so much to me."

My **ego** wasn't satisfied. I wanted to ask "Do you want to give me back the ring?" but was too afraid she'd **consent**, and that would mark the end of the contest. I could feel that I was losing, but I refused to read the writing on the wall. While there was still a chance, I wanted to keep the hope alive.

The rest of the dance went quickly and without words. We had shared what we wanted to say. I returned to Susan and explained what had taken place. But I left out my suspicions and fears about the 'writing on the wall.'

*"Do you love Tony?"*

"Just relax, Berto. Let her enjoy the evening and then see how she feels next week. Who knows. Maybe it's okay to have two boyfriends."

The last idea sounded **feasible**, but I didn't like it. It just didn't match my nature. Love is for one other, not for two. It's the feeling that a person shows to another to say that they are Number One, not Number One and Number Two. My earlier fantasy of having two girlfriends, and now Susan's **notion** of Janet having two boyfriends, sounded equally strange and unacceptable. I just couldn't change my deep-rooted childhood ideals about love so easily or suddenly. Susan sensed my **disquietude** and discontinued her train of thought. I expected that she might next suggest for me to 'prove myself' to Janet, but she never mentioned it. Perhaps she had other ideas about how love is supposed to be expressed, and **chivalry** wasn't one of them.

The evening almost ended on that note, with my desires and **anxieties** on hold until the following week, but as the prom neared the final minutes I felt a tapping on my shoulder. I turned to see Tony standing next to me.

"Can we talk a minute, Berto?" It was the first time I had ever heard him call me by my nickname, yet it sounded so familiar and flowed so naturally, one would think he had addressed me numerous times before.

"Sure, Tony, let's go outside." I **refrained** from saying "Let's step outside" for fear he would interpret it as a **veiled** threat of a showdown.

We exited the auditorium and headed towards the football field.

"Berto, how much do you like Janet?" Tony asked me in a **companionable** manner as we marched along.

"A lot, Tony. Just like you do." I wasn't in the mood for **idle** social chatter. We were two young men who could call it as we saw it.

"So what should we do?" Tony asked. "Fight each other and see who wins?"

I stopped my forward pace and **peered** into Tony's dark brown eyes. The **abruptness** of the question left me speechless for a moment. If it were that simple, I'd have **thrashed** him right then and there. But the issue wasn't really over who was stronger. It was a matter of who loved Janet more and who needed her more. Perhaps I could have said that I loved her more, but no one needed her more than Tony. Just the very fact that he asked if I wanted to fight over her indicated how much he wanted and needed her. His courage was a pleasant change from the freaked-out tobacco-head I had seen in prior weeks.

"You really do love her, don't you, Tony?" I asked **earnestly**, my eyes still glued to his.

93

*"Can we talk a minute, Berto?"*

Tony gazed down at the grass below us and shuffled his feet, moving some imaginary rocks as he sought how to phrase his next words. "Was it you who kicked over the desk?" he asked ultimately, placing his hands uncomfortably in his back pockets and glancing upward to observe my reaction. The question wasn't in line with what I had asked, but it seemed to fit perfectly into the conversation.

I nodded.

Tony then focused his attention directly on me, his voice filled with concern. "Why, Berto?" He seemed especially anxious to know why I had tried to steal the show. Or perhaps he knew the real reason already.

"I did it, Tony, because I wanted to. Because you were the perfect **scapegoat** for Mrs. A. Because if I have to choose between a fellow student and a teacher, I'll stand up for the student." But I didn't add "because I felt sorry for you." That wasn't what one guy should tell another. It would have ruined the man-to-man **tenor** of the conversation.

"I guess I should say 'Thanks' then, Berto." It was Tony's indirect way of expressing gratitude, and I didn't feel it worthwhile or fitting to advance the discussion any further. I fully grasped the **gist** of his reply, though it left me with a very odd feeling, one which melted away the competitive spirit inside. He really was an **amiable** fellow, and for the first time since our **rivalry** had begun a winner had emerged. Janet didn't need to decide; I'd decided for all of us.

I looked up at the stars to **divert** momentarily my attention from the **gravity** of the conversation and to afford myself the opportunity to frame my thoughts clearly. My next words came out with **mindful** and **heedful** consideration. "Tony, let's stay friends. And be good to Janet. She needs you a lot." I avoided making it sound like he needed her more, but then again I really didn't know that for sure. All I knew was that they shared a very special relationship, one which extended far beyond the time I had known Janet. Tony and I had **confided** in each other our innermost feelings and in doing so had built a bond of brotherly trust. We had **owned up** to one another. There were no more mysteries; there was no need for competition. We were friends.

The remainder of the evening shimmered with a **resplendent** and **roseate sanguineness** that **radiated** and **revitalized** the **vernal vivaciousness** of the Christmas prom. When I returned and spoke with Susan, our words recaptured a **consummate enchantment** that had **imbued** thoughts I felt could be **professed** to only one person in a mortal's lifetime. I had received **divine deliverance** from the **constraints** of competition and had established an eternal **amity** with those whom I treasured and **esteemed** most in my **burgeoning adolescent metamorphosis**. No, I hadn't lost. No one had lost. We were all winners.

After the conclusion of the dance I walked Susan home, **forgoing** calling my mom for a ride. The entire evening was ours, and we spent thirty **wondrous** minutes of it **engaged** in a **blissfully**

*"Was it you who kicked over the desk?"*

**rapturous promenade** through the **sylvan** shadows of the city as a **zephyr** whispered through the palm trees, stirring up the **balmy** island air. The night was cloudless and the **celestial** stars beamed their **ethereal** light upon us as only the clear Hawaiian evenings could offer – the stars never dared to come out in Owry County. Hawaii had indeed become for me a **beatific** paradise.

Yes, the prom was a learning experience. When I kissed Susan good night, a deep thrill began to grow from within, as though I had found love in everything. No longer was I worried about how others felt about me, whether Janet really liked me as much as Tony, or whether I would emerge the **victor**. We had come together as one big family – a bond of separate togetherness – and our concerns were now for one another.

Tony had returned the favor to me. We were even. He had shown me just how important it is to make friends rather than enemies, to build up rather than tear down. If only the rest of the world could learn what we learned, even Owry County might not be such a hellish place after all.

There's been no school for the week. It's Christmas vacation, climaxing with Christmas Eve tomorrow. I'll be going over to Susan's house, and she'll be coming over for dinner at my house on Christmas Day. Oh yeah, Janet and Tony are also coming. I couldn't forget to invite all my friends. After all, what's life without friends? I already know. I was born in Owry County.

**END**

# THEME SONG
## Even Odds
### *Lyrics by Raymond Karelitz*

(Male Voice #1):
I've been through it all, seen the worst a boy can see,
But I've never lost the dream of finding paradise for me.

(Male Voice #2):
I thought I had it all, but found it made me blind,
Until one day I separated truth from all the lies.

(Female Voice):
Let's even the odds and make our own tomorrow
And not think of past mistakes or dwell on heartache's sorrow.

(Chorus):
We have a future waiting, a paradise to share;
If we help those who are lost, we'll help even up the odds.

(Male Voice #1):
I've come to find others are living what I've seen,
That while my future's bright ahead, they're losing all their dreams.

(Male Voice #2):
I wish I knew why life can quickly turn so cold,
Why my dreams have turned and faded and all looks grey and old.

(Female Voice):
We have a future waiting, a paradise to share;
If we help those who are lost, we'll help even up the odds.

(Male Voice #1):
I think I've found the key to keeping hope alive;
It comes by showing others that true friendship never dies.

(Male Voice #2):
I've found a path I'd lost by chasing paper dreams;
It took my friends, it took myself to see what my life means.

(Female Voice):
Let's even the odds and make our own tomorrow
And not think of past mistakes or dwell on heartache's sorrow.

(Chorus):
We have a future waiting, a paradise to share;
And when we've helped those who were lost, then we've truly helped
even up the odds...

**Even Odds**

Glossary

The following words (deemed by the editor to be of challenging difficulty and of particular value in college writing and in entrance exams such as the S.A.T.) appear in this novel. Each word is then defined briefly in its context.

You are encouraged to purchase a marking-pen which accentuates text, highlight unfamiliar key words as they appear, and complete the highlighting process by accentuating the glossary-definition of the word.

This process of word-building through reading and highlighting will not only help you add to your vocabulary, but it will also help introduce you to the highly effective method of highlighting for future readings as well!

# Glossary
## Even Odds

**aback (taken aback)** (30) surprised and confused

**abashed** (56, 69) embarrassed

**abated** (59) diminished

**abject** (25, 45) complete

**abominable** (44) awful

**abrasively** (68) hurtfully

**abruptness** (93) unexpected suddenness

**absconded** (40) fled

**absolution** (13) forgiveness

**abstained** (56) refrained

**abstruse** (86) difficult to understand

**abyss** (25, 59) deep pit

**accentuated** (28) gave emphasis to / marked with emphasis

**acerbic** (36) sarcastic

**acrid** (59) harsh / sarcastic

**acrimonious** (36) hostile and spiteful

**adage** (45) proverb / saying

**addled** (73) confused

**adherents** (26) followers

**admonished** (55) cautioned / warned

**admonition** (89) warning

**adolescent** (24, 95) teenage

*Adonis* (12) a handsome youth [from Classical mythology]

**adulation** (77) lavish praise

**adversarial** (6, 34) bitterly opposing

**adversary** (48) enemy / opponent

**adversely** (26) negatively affected

**adversity** (57) misfortune

**affably** (36) in a friendly manner

**affiliation** (37) association

**affinity** (7) natural liking

**affront** (48) insult

**agape** (23) open-mouthed (in wonder)

**aggressive** (38) hostile / unfriendly

**agitated** (7) disturbed and upset

**air** (45, 81) manner

**akin** (18) related / similar

**alighted** (28) descended

**ally** (14) friend and associate

**aloof** (65) removed and uninvolved

**altercation** (22) angry dispute

**ambience** (86) atmosphere

**ameliorate** (27) improve

**amends** (25, 77) repayment / apology for earlier injury / harm caused

**amiable** (95) friendly

**amicably** (32) in a friendly manner

**amity** (34, 95) friendly relations

**amorous** (72, 87) loving

**ample** (41, 87) adequate

**analogous** (44, 59) comparatively similar

**anew** (25) once more / in a new way

**angst** (80) dread

**animated** (34) aroused

**animated** (51) alive

**annihilation** (12, 59) extermination / destruction

**anomaly** (80) exception

**antagonistically** (38) in a hostile manner

**antagonists** (25) rivals

**antics** (42) mischievous deeds

**antipathy** (11) dislike

**anxieties** (93) uneasiness

**anxious** (53) nervously uneasy

**aphorism** (88) proverb

**aplomb** (72) poise

**apocalypse** (84) revelation

**apostate** (14) traitor

**apprehensive** (13, 53, 80) fearfully uneasy

**apprised** (30, 79) informed

**appropriate** (24) confiscate

**appropriate** (36, 40, 49, 55, 71, 73, 86) suitable

**apropos** (81) appropriate

**apt** (55) suitable / appropriate

**arcane** (29) mysterious

**array** (2) arrangement

**articulation** (23) speech

1

**artless** (23) untalented

**ascending** (24) climbing

**ascertain** (69) establish

**ascot** (36) decorative scarf

**ascribed** (79) credited

**ashen** (13) deathly pale

**askance** (79) skeptically

**askew** (81) crookedly

**aspersion** (36) hurtful statement

**asphyxiating** (59) choking

**aspiration** (25) ambition / goal

**assertively** (85) positively and insistently / forcefully

**assiduous** (86) hardworking

**assimilating** (86) absorbing

**assumed** (45) fictitious

**atrocities** (17) cruel acts

**august** (14) awesome

**aureate** (7) golden

**auspicious** (79) favorable

**authoritarian** (44) arrogant and dictatorial

**availed** (41, 80) helped

**aversion** (7) strong dislike

**avert** (87) avoid

**badgering** (41) pestering and provoking

**badinage** (41) playful teasing

**baffled** (55) puzzled and confused

**balmy** (97) mild

**banal** (29, 86) stale / unoriginal

**bandied** (56) tossed back and forth

**baneful** (59) poisoning

**bask** (27, 63) sunbathe

**bated breath** (71) anticipation

**beacon** (57) signal

**beatific** (97) blissful

**beau** (29) sweetheart

**bedraggled** (16) sloppy / messy

**befall** (44) happen to

**befit** (24) be suitable for

**befriend** (7) make friends with

**befuddled** (22, 51, 89) confused

**bellicose** (11) hostile

**belligerent** (50) hostile / warlike

**bellowed** (44, 74) roared in a deep, loud tone

**bemused** (45) stunned / bewildered

**benefactor** (64) kindly helper

**beneficial** (33) helpful

**berated** (61) scolded

**beseechingly** (30) begging

**bespoke** (64) reflected

**betokened** (41) symbolized

**bickering** (18) quarrelling over a petty matter

**blissfully** (95) joyfully

**blithe** (17, 86) cheerful

**bluntly** (69) plainly

**bode** (12) be an omen

**bolster** (24) support

**boorish** (50) crude

**bootless** (58) futile

**bosom** (12, 56) heart / center

**bovine** (48) dull and slow

**bozos** (61) [slang] clowns

**braggadocio** (28) empty bragging

**braggarts** (28) bragging people

**brash** (42) tastelessly rude

**bridle** (48) restrain

**browbeating** (14, 61) bullying

**brunt** (25) full force

**brusquely** (23) rudely sudden and forceful

**buffoons** (74) clowns

**bugbear** (41) source of (usually groundless) fears

**bumpkins** (50) unsophisticated rustics ("hillbillies")

**burgeoning** (95) flourishing

**bustling** (86) busy and active

**cajones** (41) [Spanish / slang] guts (loosely)

**callous** (72) unfeeling

**callow** (64) naïve / immature

**candidly** (69, 91) honestly and openly

**candor** (72) honesty and directness

**captious** (79) faultfinding

**captivatingly** (29) fascinatingly

**castigation** (79) scolding

**catastrophic** (89) disastrous

**catbird seat** (73) advantageous position

*Catch-22* (49) no-win

**caustic** (79) stingingly sarcastic

**celebrity** (77) famous person

**celestial** (97) heavenly

**chafed** (47) irritated

**champion** (23) fight for

**chaperoning** (56) escorting

**charismatic** (12) fascinatingly attractive

**chary** (89) cautiously watchful

**chastising** (37, 49) criticizing severely

**chauvinistic** (34) intolerant and prejudiced

**checked** (67) restrained

**cherish** (80) hold dear

**cherubic** (28) angelic / youthfully innocent

**chic** (74) stylish

**chicanery** (81) trickery and deception

**chiding** (63) scolding mildly

**chimerical** (7) unrealistically fanciful

**chivalry** (93) medieval code of gallantry and courtesy

**chortled** (47) chuckled and chortled

**chthonian** (80) infernal

**circuitous** (74) roundabout

**circumspect** (89) cautious

**civility** (12) courtesy

**clad** (28) clothed

**clamor** (42) outcry

**clandestine** (28) secret

**cliché** (77) overused expression

*Clint Eastwood* (12) 1970s-1980s "tough guy" actor

**clique** (51) group

**cloak** (90) cover

**coercion** (11) intimidation

**cogitating** (64) thinking over

**cognizant** (2) aware

**cohesive** (26) unified

**cohorts** (17) associates / companions

**collaboration** (81) working together

**commenced** (80) began

**commiseration** (64) sympathy

**commute** (6) travel

**companionable** (93) friendly

**compassion** (64, 72) a feeling of sympathy and understanding for another

**compassionate** (57) kindhearted

**compatriots** (69) companions

**compelled** (40, 79, 90) driven / urged on

**complaisant** (34) friendly and helpful

**complexion** (51) appearance

**comportment** (44) conduct

**comprehended** (64) understood

**comprehensive** (51) complete

**comrade** (14) friend

**conceded** (80) acknowledged

**concisely** (67) to the point

**conclusively** (71) decisively final

**concur** (81) agree

**condemnatory** (85) criticizing

**condescending** (74) acting as if superior and lowering oneself to address another

**condone** (44) overlook / tolerate

**confidant** (4) person confided in

**confided** (95) revealed secrets trustfully

**confidential** (27, 55) intimate

**confounding** (72) baffling

**confreres** (2) cohorts / associated

**confront** (80, 90) challenge face to face (in battle)

**confrontation** (13, 30) unfriendly encounter

**congenially** (69) in a friendly manner

**congregated** (81) gathered together

**conjectural** (64) speculated

**conjunction** (12) union

**conjure** (47, 58, 80) devise / imagine

**conquest** (34) victory

**consensus** (81) agreement

**consent** (91) agree to what was suggested

**consequential** (53) significant in its consequences

**consort** (2) mingle / socialize

**conspiring** (12) scheming

**constraints** (40, 95) restraints

**consummate** (67, 95) perfect / supreme

**contemplate** (11) consider deeply and seriously

**contend** (73) struggle / compete

**contentiously** (22) quarreling

**contriving** (2) plotting

**conversant** (55) knowledgeable

**converse** (27, 69, 89) chat

**conversion** (75) change

**convey** (49) communicate

**convivial** (86) sociable

**convolutedly** (74) intricately

**cope** (67) manage

**coquettish** (41) flirtatious

**cordial** (12, 86) friendly

**cordoned** (6) blockaded / obstructed

**corsage** (79) a small bouquet of flowers

**coterie** (42) clique

**countenance** (25) outward (facial) appearance

**covenant** (80) solemn agreement

**covert** (64) hidden and secretive

**cow** (14, 67) intimidate

**cower** (12, 80) crouch in fear

**coyly** (18, 40) pretending to be shy and bashful

**crafty** (1) cunning

**craven** (13) cowardly

**crestfallen** (40) dejected / depressed

**cringe** (13) cower

**cronies** (30, 51) friends / associated

**crucifixion** (44) painful torture

**cultivated** (42, 56) develop

**curbed** (79, 90) controlled

**curt** (68) rudely brief

**dank** (25) unpleasantly damp

**daredevil** (80) recklessly bold / adventurous

**dauntlessly** (13) fearlessly

*Dear Abby* (19) advice giving columnist

**debase** (74) degrade

**deface** (61) damage

**defecting** (79) deserting

**deferentially** (75) courteously respectful

**defiance** (11) act of resistance

**defile** (79) spoil

**definitive** (53) complete and reliable

**defuse** (49, 63) make harmless / powerless

**defy** (37) challenge

**degradation** (75) shame and humiliation

**dehumanizing** (74) degrading

**dejectedly** (23) in a gloomy and depressed manner

**deleterious** (58) harmful

**deliberate** (47, 68, 71) carefully considered

**delinquents** (17) lawbreakers

**deliverance** (95) rescue from danger

**delude** (23, 73) deceive

**delusions** (17) misconceptions

**demeanor** (40) outward manner / behavior

**demonically** (47) devilishly

**demoralized** (75) stripped of one's spirit and courage

**demure** (27) bashful

**depravity** (49) moral corruption

**derelicts** (22) outcasts

**deriding** (30) ridiculing

**derisive** (47, 74) mocking

**derive** (50) originate

**descried** (80) noticed

**desecration** (37) disrespect by defiling

desist (12) discontinue

desolation (25) loneliness

despair (58) hopelessness

despicably (74) disgracefully

despot (74) tyrant

destitute (12) poor

desultory (58) random / aimless

deteriorated (44) worsened

devastating (91) destructive

deviltry (59) reckless mischief

devoid (74) lacking

dialectic (79) logically presented (in argumentation)

diametrically (74) direct / complete

didactic (87) instructional

diffident (75) bashful / lacking confidence

dignity (23) honor

digressively (18) straying from the main topic

dilemma (56) difficult situation, problem or choice

diminutive (16) tiny

dingy (44, 74) dirty and shabby

disabuse (14) enlighten

discern (80) distinguish / identify

discompose (29) fluster

disconcerted (80) upset / confused

discordant (83) clashing

discourse (23) communication / conversation

discreetly (91) carefully / thoughtfully prudent

disdainful (11) scornful

disencumbered (48) liberated

disheveled (42, 74) messy

disparage (74, 79) belittle

dispirit (74) make feel dejected

disported (40) amused himself

disposition (22, 42, 50, 69) spirit or nature / mood

disquieting (53) upsetting

disquietude (93) state of uneasiness / agitation

dissembling (90) masking

dissipated (63) became less concentrated

dissipation (58) overindulgence

distorted (48) altered the meaning of

distractible (71) easily disturbed

diverse (4) varied

diversion (40, 83) turning away from the main point

divert (95) distract

divine (42, 95) supremely good

docile (27) manageably obedient

dolefully (74) sadly

domain (80) territory

domestic (6) relating to the home

domicile (6) residence

domination (6) control

domineeringly (34) overbearingly controlling

doughty (11) fearless and determined

dour (45) gloomy / sullen

downy (29) soft

draped (6) hung loosely

dreaded (80) feared

dubiously (79) skeptically

dulcetly (41) sweet-sounding

dumbfounded (14) speechless with amazement

duping (81) fooling

dwelt (86) directed one's attention

dynamically (23) forceful and energetic

earnest (14, 72, 93) seriousness and with sincere feeling

ebullience (75) enthusiasm

eccentric (28) unusual

eclectic (2) diverse

eeriness (44) frightening weirdness / strangeness

**effectuate** (37) accomplish

**effervescence** (69) liveliness

**effusion** (69) outpouring

**ego** (23, 24, 87, 91) self-pride

**egotist** (17) self-centered person

**elaborated** (65) explained in greater detail

**elation** (28) ecstasy

**elicit** (75) bring forth

**elite** (83) socially superior

**eloquence** (23) persuasive and effective manner of speech

**elusive** (86) hard to catch / difficult to understand

**Elysian** (7, 28) heavenly

**embark** (22) begin / start

**embellished** (7) enhanced / decorated

**embroiled** (44) involved

**empathetic** (71) sharing feelings

**empyreal** (59) heavenly

**emulate** (25, 57) imitate (and hope to equal / surpass)

**enchanting** (7) charming

**enchantment** (95) charm

**encounter** (13, 23, 81, 90) meet

**encroach** (80) intrude / trespass

**endeared** (30) attracted

**endearingly** (17) attractively

**endeavor** (80, 63) serious determined effort

**endure** (1, 26) tolerate

**engage** (6, 36) enter into a challenge

**engage** (95) involve

**engaging** (50) charming

**engender** (89) produced / gave life to

**engineering** (17) planning and organizing

**engrossed** (29) deeply absorbed and interested

**enigmas** (47) puzzles

**enlighten** (75) enrich spiritually through instruction

**enlightened** (79) spiritually aware

**enlivened** (56) cheered up

**enrapturing** (29) captivating

**enriched** (24) strengthened

**ensure** (47) guarantee

**entertained** (71) considered

**entourage** (14) group of traveling companions

**entranced** (77) hypnotically fascinating

**envisaging** (29) picturing

**envision** (18, 68) picture in one's mind

**epiphany** (75) uplifting revelation

**epithets** (79) curses ("four-letter" words)

**epitome** (28) model / ideal representation

**epitomize** (45) represent ideally

**equanimity** (11) composure

**equilibrium** (63) balance

**erotically** (41) sexually suggestive

**errant** (2) wandering

**erring** (37) straying in error

**erroneously** (64) mistakenly

**escapade** (2, 25) carefree, reckless adventure

**eschew** (17) avoid

**esoteric** (47, 80) mysterious

**espied** (36, 80) caught sight of / noticed

**esprit de corps** (56) team spirit

**essay** (59) attempted

**esteemed** (95) highly regarded

**estranged** (19) separated / feeling no close attraction to

**ethereal** (97) heavenly

**euphoric** (28) bliss

**evade** (11) avoid

**eventuated** (75) resulted

**evident** (71) clear / obvious

**exalted** (83) uplifted

**exasperation** (59) frustration

**excelled** (57) performed outstandingly

**excoriate** (79) condemn

**excruciatingly** (59) intensely painful

**execration** (50) cursing

**exhort** (59) urge

**explicitly** (67) specifically / clearly

**exploits** (59) deeds / accomplishments

**expulsion** (59) ejection

**extricate** (79) liberate

**exuberantly** (75) joyfully and excitedly

**exudes** (11) gives off

**exultantly** (16) triumphantly joyful

**exultation** (36) extreme joy

**fabricated** (7) assembled artistically

**facilely** (73) easily

**fanciful** (41) wildly imaginative

**fancy** (30) showy / sudden notion

**faring** (72) getting along

**fathom** (86) comprehend

**faux pas** (89) blunder

**fawning** (20) showing servile fondness

**fearsome** (13) terrifying

**feasible** (81, 93) workable or manageable / able
  to be done / accomplished

**feckless** (18) ineffective

**feign** (55, 81) pretend

**felicitous** (87) joyful

**fellowship** (2) companionship

**fervent** (41) impassioned

**fervidly** (61) urgently and passionately

**festered** (47) developed and grew

**festive** (12) joyous / merry

**fiasco** (59) disastrous failure

**fickle** (12) unpredictably changeable

**filch** (79) steal

**finale** (59) conclusion

**fisticuffs** (36) fist-fight

**flagrant** (59) deliberate and shameless

**flair** (28) stylish

**flamboyant** (27) elaborate and showy

**flanked** (13, 24) covered on each side; at each
  side

**flaring** (51) broadening (in anger)

**flaunt** (77) show off

**fledglings** (2) beginners / novices

**flustered** (22, 79) nervously confused

**flux** (48) continuous change

**foe** (44) enemy / opponent

**foibles** (55) minor faults

**foisted** (20) forced uninvitedly on

**fold** (11) group / flock

**fomented** (56) stirred up

**foolhardy** (37, 80) recklessly bold

**forbidding** (44) unfriendly

**foreman** (58) boss

**forestalling** (45) preventing

**forged** (45) gave shape to

**forgoing** (95) doing without / giving up

**forlorn** (49) depressed / deserted

**formidable** (14) fearfully impressive

**forsaken** (49) rejected / abandoned

**forthcoming** (81) approaching / coming up

**forthwith** (64) immediately

**fortuitous** (48) unexpectedly lucky

**forward** (68) rudely bold

**fracas** (18) disorderly disturbance

**fractious** (44) irritable

**frank** (67, 78) open and direct

**fraternity** (2) brotherhood

**frittering** (11) wasting

**frivolously** (47) in a silly, foolish manner

**frolicsome** (40) playing in a happy, lighthearted manner

**fulmination** (51) expression of rage

**futility** (23, 33) uselessness and hopelessness

**galled** (40) annoyed

**germane** (55) relevant

**gibe** (41) taunt

**giddy** (75) silly

**gist** (95) main idea / point

**glaring** (32) staring angrily

**gleefully** (14) merrily / joyfully

**glistening** (87) sparkling

**gloaming** (40) twilight

**glower** (11) stare angrily

**gnome** (63) dwarf-like character

**goad** (27, 36) spur / urge on

**gorgeous** (40) beautiful / attractive

**grandiose** (17) magnificent

**gravity** (95) seriousness / importance

**gregarious** (1) sociable

**grim** (44) stern / cruel

**groggily** (44) dazed / in a stunned manner

**grovel** (14) crawl (as in a display of self-worthlessness)

**gruesome** (48) horribly disgusting

**gruff** (47) crudely abrupt

**guardedly** (48) cautiously

**guileless** (41) straightforward

*Guinevere* (77) queen of legendary Camelot

**habitats** (4) territories

*Hades* (59) Hell

**halcyon** (75) peaceful

**harassing** (14) tormenting

**hardship** (69) suffering

**hardy** (90) sturdy

**haughty** (63) arrogant

**hauteur** (32) haughty manner

**haven** (7) refuge

**hedonistic** (17) pleasure-seeking

**heedful** (95) attentive

**heedless** (4053) thoughtless

**hefty** (30) strong

**heralded** (87) announced

**hindsight** (63) looking back into the past

**histrionics** (63, 90) theatrical drama

**hoodlum** (33) young gangster

**hooligan** (17) hoodlum

**hubris** (32) excessive pride

**hulking** (47) massive

**humble** (67) modest / gentle

**humility** (32) humbleness

**hypocrite** (90) a person who acts contrary to what he believes

**idiosyncrasies** (55) peculiarities

**idle** (4, 27, 93) meaningless

**ignoble** (25) shameless

**ignominious** (2, 79) shameless

**ill will** (48) bitter feelings

**illuminate** (29) glow

**imbroglio** (45) entanglement

**imbued** (95) filled / saturated

**immensely** (58) hugely

**immersed** (51) absorbed deeply

**imminent** (45) approaching / near at hand / happening soon

**immutable** (79) unchangeable

**impacted** (64) affected

**impassioned** (51) passionate

**impassively** (81) lacking emotion

**impelled** (58, 91) urged forward / propelled

**imperious** (51) domineering

**impetuous** (37) impulsive

**implored** (23) begged urgently

**import** (86) significance

**imposing** (48) impressive

**imprecations** (37) curses

**impudence** (47) rudeness

**impugnation** (30) verbal attack

**inadvertently** (36) unintentionally

**inauspicious** (41) unfavorable

**incapacitated** (48) crippled

**incendiary** (44) inflammatory

**incensed** (85) enraged

**inconspicuously** (45) not seeking notice from others

**inconstant** (80) changing

**incorrigibles** (37) delinquents

**incredulously** (32, 79) skeptically and in disbelief

**incurious** (80) not curious

**indefatigable** (56) tireless

**indifferent** (44) unconcerned / uninterested

**indignation** (14) resentment

**indignity** (74) insult

**indiscernible** (32) undistinguishable

**indulge** (41) oblige / cater

**inebriated** (18) drunk

**ineffectual** (23, 81) without decisive effect

**inevitable** (29, 86, 90) unavoidable / inescapable

**inextricable** (44) hopelessly entangled

**infallible** (42) indestructible

**infantile** (17) childish

**infernal** (25) hellish

**inferno** (44) oven / fiery pit

**infiltrated** (59) entered

**ingenuous** (28) unsophisticated / natural and honest

**ingratiated** (48) charmed

**inhibited** (89) restrained

**inhospitable** (45) unfriendly

**inimical** (44) hostile

**inimitable** (40) unique

**initial** (69) first

**initiate** (30, 59) begin / originate

**injudicious** (79) unwise

**innocuous** (34) harmless

**innovative** (24) new and creative

**innuendos** (34) indirect (usually negative) references and comments / hints and rumors

**inquisitive** (84) curious

**inscrutable** (47) incomprehensible

**insidious** (34, 67) sneaky and devious

**insolent** (56) disrespectful

**instigate** (6) initiate / provoke

**insufferable** (17) intolerable

**integral** (57) essential

**intemperance** (55) lack of moderation

**intent** (75) determined / insistent

**interjecting** (89) inserted / added in

**interminable** (23) exhaustingly endless

**interrogation** (84) formal questioning

**intertwined** (18) bound together

**intimate** (7, 18, 55, 75) close and deeply personal

**intimidate** (11, 13) cause fear (as by threatening)

**intoxication** (6, 44) drunkenness

**intractable** (17) stubborn

**intrigue** (67) scheming

**introspective** (27, 58) self-analyzing

**intrusiveness** (55) interference

**intuitively** (55) naturally, without need for deep thought

**invaluable** (49) priceless

**invasive** (67) intruding

**inveigle** (56) entice

**inventive** (6) skillfully original

**inviolable** (7) free from violation

**inviolate** (80) sacred

**irascible** (77) bad-tempered

**irate** (33) enraged

**irked** (37) irritated

**ironic** (68) contrary to expectation / incongruous

**ironies** (77) seemingly inconsistent but yet natural occurrences

**irreconcilable** (1) unable to restore peace and friendship

**irretrievable** (12) unrecoverable

*Jack the Ripper* (45) infamous 19th century British criminal

**jaundiced** (56) jealous

**jauntily** (28) spiritedly

**jovial** (69, 89) happy and merry

**jubilant** (36) joyful

**juggernaut** (13) large, overpowering force

**justification** (79) answer

**juvenile** (77) childish / immature

**juvenile** (2, 24, 44) designated for minors

**juvenile** (13) young

**ken** (86) range of knowledge

kindle (37) fuel

kindling (44) arousing / exciting

kindred spirits (56) close friends ("soul mates")

kinship (75) close relationship

kinsmen (34) relatives

knavish (34) dishonest ("good for nothing")

lambasted (33) scolded severely

lambent (6, 86) softly bright

languorous (42) listless

lascivious (34) indecent / lustful

laudable (23) praiseworthy

laughingstock (74) object of ridicule

lest (85) for fear that

levy (37) impose

liberated (25) set free

lingering (48, 67, 71) remaining

lionized (12) praised and admired

listlessness (44) sluggishness

litigation (16) filing a lawsuit

livid (51) enraged

longed (91) desired

luminary (74) celebrity

lures (53) attracts

lust (17, 34) intense desire

machinations (81) schemes

macho (14) masculine (usually exaggeratedly so)

maelstrom (48, 73) whirlpool

magnanimity (57) noble generosity and charity

malaise (44) mental uneasiness / general weakness

malcontent (17) a person dissatisfied with conditions as they are

malefactor (47) evildoer

malevolent (24) mean

malign (47) slander

manifest (59) express

manifest (90) obvious

manifestation (64) display

manipulate (47, 58) manage shrewdly or deviously

mannered (90) affected / artificial

marionette (64) puppet controlled by strings

*Mark Antony* (23) Roman orator

markedly (75) noticeably

martyr (42, 75) person who suffers openly in behalf of a belief / cause

masochistic (42) finding pleasure from being abused

masterminded (67) planned

maternal (4) motherly

matriarch (56) female ruler

measured (23) carefully thought out

meekly (75) submissively

megalomaniac (17) person suffering from delusions of grandeur

melancholy (50) sadness

melee (34) brawl

mellifluous (12) sweet-sounding

mercurial (80) impulsive / changeable

metamorphosis (75, 95) complete change

metaphysical (75) supernaturally transcendent

mien (12) manner

mincing (65) moderating / restraining

mindful (44, 55, 95) carefully watchful and aware

mingling (49) socializing

minions (20, 58) submissive followers / lower class subjects

minuscule (27) tiny

mired (49) bogged down

misconstrued (80) misinterpreted

miscreants (49) evildoers

misgivings (7193) doubts / fears

misguided (38, 63) misdirected

mitigate (25) lessen the severity of

**mockingly** (32, 48) teasingly

**modicum** (73) minimum amount

**mollified** (56) pacified

**momentous** (53, 71) extremely important

**monotonous** (1) boring

**morass** (49) bog / troublesome situation

**mortal** (77) deadly

**motivated** (17) stimulated

**motive** (64) reason

**muddled** (71) confused

**mull** (64) think / ponder

**multitude** (71) large number

**mum** (18, 63) not saying a word

**mundane** (47, 71, 86) day-to-day

**mustered** (41) assembled / gathered together

**mutually** (29) shared

**mystified** (65) baffled

**naïve** (24) not sophisticated / street-smart

**narcissistic** (12) overly concerned and interested in oneself

**navigating** (42) managing the course of

**ne'er-do-wells** (2) idle, worthless persons

**nebulous** (86) hazy / vague

**nefarious** (59) wicked

**nemesis** (40) opponent / rival (often, a superior one)

**nettled** (13) annoyingly provoked

**nonchalance** (23) unconcerned

**nonchalantly** (32) in a cool, unconcerned manner

**nondescript** (80) inconspicuous

**nonentity** (79) nobody (a "zero")

**nonpareil** (40) person without equal

**nonplussed** (68) baffled / perplexed

**normalcy** (51) state of being back to normal

**notion** (71, 93) idea / conception

**notoriety** (83) bad reputation

**novel** (59) new and different

**noxiously** (59) harmfully

**nurturing** (41) developing / promoting

**obligatory** (81) morally / legally required

**oblige** (50, 72) accommodate

**obliging** (56) helpful

**oblivious** (40, 49) totally unaware

**obscurity** (63) state of being forgotten

**obtuse** (49) slow-witted / stupid

**ogle** (33) glance at amorously

**omnipotence** (17) complete power

**onerous** (23, 56) burdensome

**opportune** (14, 41, 56, 91) favorable / suitable

**opprobrious** (37) shameful

**opted** (65) chose

**oratory** (23) eloquence

**ostensibly** (12) apparently

**ostracized** (68) shunned / rejected

**otiose** (23) ineffective

**outlandish** (55, 80) bizarre

**overt** (75, 90) obvious

**own up** (90, 95) admit to / acknowledge

**palatable** (69) appetizing

**palliate** (44) relieve

**palpable** (75) noticeable

**palpitations** (48) rapid heartbeats

**paltry** (22) insignificant / worthless

**panache** (28) showiness

**pandemonium** (44) chaos

**pander** (17) cater

**pang** (56, 72) sudden, sharp pain

**paramount** (61) foremost

**paranoia** (67) feelings of fear and distrust

**pariah** (25, 80) social outcast

**parochial** (34) narrow-minded

**passively** (44) submissively

**pathetic** (25, 42) pitiful

**patronizing** (12) speaking down to

**peccadillo** (40) minor

**peer** (49, 77, 93) look searchingly

**peers** (37, 80) fellow classmates / associates

**peevish** (50) irritable

**pellucidly** (73) clearly

**perambulate** (28) stroll

**percussion** (57) impact

**perdition** (44) eternal damnation

**peremptory** (24) absolute and without debate or argument

**perfunctory** (81) superficially

**perish** (87) die

**pernicious** (45) dangerous

**perpetrate** (25, 51, 81) commit

**perplexed** (51, 84) confused and puzzled

**perverse** (13) wrong-headed

**perverted** (48) distorted

**pestering** (41) bothering

**petrified** (13, 47) scared stiff / frozen in fear

**petty** (1, 57) trivial

**philistine** (17) uncultured

**pilfer** (2) steal

**pined** (47) longed / craved

**piqued** (11, 71) aroused

**pitch-dark** (6) extremely dark

**pithy** (86) concise and meaningful

**placid** (16, 80) calm and peaceful

**plaid** (49) crisscrossed-pattern

**pleasantries** (86) polite remarks

**plethora** (34) overabundance

**ploys** (25) strategies

**plushly** (6) luxuriously and with a velvet softness

**ply** (58) follow

**polarized** (27) divided into opposite extremes

**pompous** (17) self-important

**ponder** (14, 71) think deeply

**portentous** (22) significant

**poseur** (20) showoff

**possessed** (37) obsessed

**posture** (65) bearing

**pragmatic** (87) practical

**precariously** (73) hazardously

**precipitately** (53) hastily

**precocious** (69) mentally advanced

**predators** (45) hunters

**predetermined** (24) determined beforehand

**predilections** (17) preferences

**preliminarily** (36) in an introductory manner

**preoccupied** (65) focused in interest / absorbed in thought

**preordained** (42) predestined

**prepossessing** (12) attractive / charming

**prescient** (63) predicted beforehand

**pressing** (56) urgent

**pretentious** (58) boastfully showy

**prey** (24) victim

*Prince Charming* (4) a fairy-tale prince

**pristine** (28) pure and untouched

**privy** (80) aware of a secret

**probing** (55) searching

**problematic** (67) uncertain

**procession** (32) orderly march

**proclaim** (16, 20) declare

**prodding** (30) urging / encouragement

**professed** (195) claimed

**proffered** (14) offered

**proliferate** (67) multiply

**promenade** (97) leisurely walk

**prompted** (90) stimulated

**prosaically** (87) unimaginatively

**prostrate** (16) lying flat

**protracted** (36) extended / lengthened

**proverbial** (79) containing a practical message

**provocation** (30) creating anger / resentment

**provoke** (11) stir / arouse

**prowess** (34) superior ability / skill

**proximity** (6) nearness

**prudent** (81) wise and sensible

**prying** (67) meddlesome / intrusive

**puerile** (25, 81) childish

**pugnacious** (36) quarrelsome

**puissant** (80) powerful

**pummeled** (9) beat up

**purgatory** (47) temporary hell

**purge** (59) cleanse

**purloining** (25) stealing

**qualms** (48) misgivings

**quandary** (67) dilemma

**quashed** (51) suppressed

**queasy** (63) nauseous

**quell** (32, 48) subdue

**querulously** (59) in a complaining manner

**query** (53, 91) question (to solve a doubt)

**quests** (86) searches

**quibbling** (50) arguing trivially

**quixotic** (17, 83) idealistic / unrealistic

**quizzical** (40) perplexed

**rabble** (36) mob / commoners

**radiant** (72, 86) shining bright

**radiated** (17, 95) emitted

**rage** (22) violent, hostile anger

**railed** (36) complained bitterly

**rambling** (18, 86) speaking aimlessly and at length

**ramshackle** (13) poorly constructed / run-down

**rankled** (30, 37, 69) irritated

**rapport** (80) understanding

**rapt** (87) absorbed

**rapturous** (24, 97) ecstatic

**rational** (73) reasonable and logical

**rationale** (64) body of reasons supporting a belief

**rationalized** (78) justified / explained (often as an excuse or accommodating explanation)

**readily** (81) promptly and willingly

**realm** (63) domain

**rebuffed** (68) snubbed

**reciprocate** (44) do in return

**reckoning** (90) final judgment / settlement

**reclusive** (4) secluded

**reconciled** (77) made peace / friendship with

**reconciliation** (79) restoring to friendship or unity

**recondite** (86) profound ("deep")

**recreant** (80) coward

**recumbent** (87) lying down

**redeem** (58, 87) rescue / reform or set straight

**redemption** (33) liberation from sin

**red-handed** (81) in the criminal act

**redolent** (17) reminiscent

**reenacting** (28) replaying

**refractory** (51) stubborn / unmanageable

**refrained** (56, 93) held oneself back

**refuge** (45) shelter from danger and trouble

**regurgitating** (79) spit up / vomit

**rejuvenated** (71) restored youthful vigor and energy

**rekindled** (55) reawakened / restarted

**relishes** (27) enjoys greatly

**reminisce** (86) recall past experiences

**remonstration** (13) protest

**rendezvous** (27) prearranged meeting

**repose** (56) peace / calmness

**reproving** (85) scolding

**requite** (37) pay back

**reservation** (80) doubt

**reserve** (28) self-restraint / shyness

**residue** (49) remaining trace

**resigned** (61) gave in without resistance

**resilience** (69) ability to bounce back

**resolution** (67) solution to a problem

**resolved** (51, 65, 71, 79) decided / settled

**resonated** (24) gave off a sound

**resourcefully** (6) inventively / creatively

**resplendent** (95) dazzling / sparkling

**retaliate** (41) seek revenge

**reticence** (79) shyness

**retorted** (37, 56) replied sharply

**retrogression** (12) going backward and (usually) to a worse condition

**revel** (77) delight greatly

**revelatory** (79) discovery

**revelry** (34) loud partying

**reveres** (12) respects and fears

**reverie** (29) daydream

**revitalized** (71, 95) renewed in energy

**rhapsodic** (29) ecstatic

**rhetoric** (22) polished but insincere speech

**ribald** (34) vulgar

**righteousness** (23) moral standards of good behavior

**riled** (33) angered

**rival** (12, 13, 23, 37) competitor

**rivalry** (34, 95) competition

**riveted** (29) engrossed

**roguish** (25) dishonest / villainous

**roseate** (95) optimistic

**row** (36) noisy quarrel / dispute

**ruffians** (27) bullies

**ruminations** (71) lengthy meditations

**sabotage** (77) undermine

**saccharine** (20) sweet

**safeguarding** (29) protecting

**salvation** (33) means of liberation

**sanction** (55) approve

**sanctuary** (45) place of refuge

**sanguinary** (13) bloody

**sanguineness** (95) optimism

**sarcastically** (56) mockingly / with a biting wit

**sardonically** (48) cruelly and sarcastically

**satiate** (17) satisfy fully

**saucy** (18) boldly disrespectful

**sauntering** (86) strolling

**savior** (4) rescuer

**savor** (4, 27) enjoy

**scamps** (50) rascals

**scantily** (28) minimally

**scapegoat** (95) victim

**scuffling** (61) squabbling

**scurried** (65) moved quickly

**scurrilous** (37) coarse and offensive

**sedulously** (42) diligently

**seething** (6) boiling in anger

**self-assured** (27, 42, 80) self-confident

**self-deprecating** (12) very modest

**self-possessed** (80) calm

**self-reliant** (67) depending upon oneself for strength and direction

**semblance** (74) outward appearance

**sensuous** (41) pleasurable

**serene** (80) calm and peaceful

**servility** (13, 20) submissive obedience

**shag** (6) rough / matted

**sheepishly** (20) in an embarrassed manner

**shepherd** (40) watch over

*Shirley Temple* (77) popular child movie star ("complex" alluded to rumors that many child stars sought to emulate her)

**sibling** (29, 56, 75) brother / sister

**singularly** (59) unique

**sinister** (38) mysteriously evil / threatening trouble or harm

*Sir Lancelot* (77) gallant knight who secretly romanced Guinevere

**sitcom** (20) situation-comedy

**skirmish** (37) encounter / brief fight

**slighting** (72) snubbing

**slurred** (6) unclear

**smirk** (41) sneer

**sneered** (74) looked at mockingly

**snicker** (74) laugh in a sly, sarcastic or snide manner

**snug** (54) tight / comfortable

**sober** (9) rational

**sober up** (63) become sober (in context: stop drinking, etc.)

**sojourn** (49, 79) visit

**solace** (56) comfort

**solemnly** (72) in a serious and honest manner

**solicitously** (47) in a concerned manner

**solicitude** (50, 90) concern

**solitude** (27) isolation

**somberly** (71) seriously

**somnolent** (68) drowsy

**sophistication** (12) worldliness / refinement

**sophomoric** (71) immature

**sordid** (25) disreputable

**spectral** (41) ghostly

**spittoon** (33, 44) a bowl used to spit into

**spleen** (51) spitefulness

**splendor** (59) brilliance / magnificence

**splenetic** (59) irritable / spiteful

**spontaneously** (55, 91) out of impulse and without any forethought

**sprightly** (68) lively / animated

**squabble** (18, 25) quarrel

**squalid** (25) unclean

**squarely** (68) at an even level

**stalk** (45) hunt / track prey

**stanch** (69) stop the flow of

**standoffish** (65) unsociable / distant

**startling** (51) shocking

**stately** (36) elegant and respectable

**status** (22) position

**stealthy** (80) sneaky

**stem** (48) derive

**stereotypical** (84) generalized

**stern** (22) harsh and expressing displeasure

**stifle** (69) hold back / restrain

**stiletto** (11) thick bladed dagger

**stoke** (41) stir up

**straightforwardly** (535, 89) directly

**stride (in stride)** (18) without becoming upset

**strides** (77) steps

**stringent** (49) strict

**stupefied** (32) stunned

**stygian** (80) infernal

**stymied** (41) baffled

**subdued** (89) toned down / refrained from showiness

**subjugating** (75) enslaved

**sublime** (41) glorious / superb

**submission** (67) yielding to the power of another

**subsided** (61) decreased in intensity

**subtle** (27, 32, 40, 85) not obvious or direct / faint but noticeable

**succinctly** (49) clear and concise

**succumbed** (41) surrendered to a superior force

**sulking** (18) feeling resentful and gloomy

**sullen** (45) gloomy and resentful

**summon** (81) call forth

**supercilious** (12) pompous / arrogant

**superficial** (16) not serious or deep

*Superman* (8, 24) comic-book hero character

**supine** (63) lying on one's back

**supplicating** (63) begging

**surreptitiously** (40) secretly

**swaggering** (28) strutting with an insolent air

**swoon** (12) faint

**sycophantic** (77) servilely flattering

**sylvan** (97) forest-like / wooded

**tacit** (64) unspoken, yet clearly communicated

**taunt** (41) challenge through insults

**teetered** (51) seesawed

**tenebrous** (59) dark and gloomy

**tenor** (95) essence

**testy** (77) irritable

**tête-à-tête** (7) private chat

*The New Kids* (4) 1980s youthful rock band

**thrashed** (93) beaten soundly

**timbre** (24) tonal quality of a sound

**timely** (81) well-timed

**timidly** (48, 79) in a fearfully shy manner

**timorous** (16) fearfully shy

**tittered** (55) giggled nervously

**toadies** (27) servile flatterers

**torpidly** (49) sluggishly

**torturous** (59) painfully agonizing

**toxins** (59) poisons

**tractable** (56) easily manageable

**trait** (57) distinguishing feature / characteristic

**tranquillity** (11) peace

**transfixed** (28) spellbound

**transformational** (75) involving change

**transformed** (56, 80) changed in appearance

**transgression** (48) sin

**transpire** (73) occur

**transposition** (80) interchange

**traversable** (73) able to travel along / move across

**tremulous** (24) shaking

**trials** (26) distressful situations

**tribulations** (26) suffering

**trifle** (27) little bit

**trite** (18) overused and unimaginative / meaningless and uninteresting

**truculent** (36) belligerent

**turbulent** (73) stormy

**turning yellow** (13) showing cowardly signs

*Twilight Zone* (32) 1960s television series known for its eerie plots

**tyrant** (58) dictators

**unabashedly** (30) shamelessly

**unaffectedly** (89) genuinely

**unassuming** (28) not showy / conceited

**unavailing** (34) of no benefit

**unbridled** (44) wild and uncontrolled

**uncensored** (69) not suppressed

**unceremoniously** (50) rudely and abruptly

**unconstrained** (4) not restrained

**unctuous** (13) fawning

**undaunted** (69) not easily discouraged

**uneasy** (20, 86) uncomfortable

**unencumbered** (83) freed from burden

**unequivocally** (49) clearly

**uneventful** (27) ordinary

**unfounded** (56) groundless

**ungraciously** (37) discourteously

**uninhibited** (75) not constrained

**unmitigated** (53) absolute

**unnerve** (67) strip of courage or strength

**unobtrusive** (27) modest / reserved

**unorthodox** (40) not traditionally acceptable

**unravel** (47, 77) solve

**unruffled** (36) calm

**unsavory** (17) unappealing

**untimely** (56) unfortunate

**unwarranted** (72) unjustified / groundless

**uplifting** (12) inspiring

**upshot** (59) outcome

**upstages** (61, 63) distracts and takes over the main attention

**upstart** (25) eager novice

**usurping** (80) snatching

**utopia** (27) paradise

**vacantly** (44) blankly

**vacillate** (53, 73) waver / indecision

**vacuous** (74) empty / empty-headed

**validate** (55) prove to be accurate and true

**vandalism** (59) willful, malicious destruction of property

**vandalous** (37) maliciously destructive

**vapid** (29) dull and stale

**veiled** (67, 93) masked / concealed

**venomous** (6) spiteful

**vent** (23, 51) express

**veracious** (77) truthful

**verge** (72) edge / border

**verily** (63) truly

**veritable** (58) actual

**vernal** (17, 95) youthful

**vestige** (23) remaining trace

**vexed** (13) irritated / annoyed

**vicarious** (17) indirect

**vicissitudes** (73) sudden changes

**victor** (97) winner

**vigilant** (67) alert

**vigorously** (23) energetically

**vilify** (79) slander

**virility** (34) masculinity

**virulence** (6) malice

**viscerally** (85) instinctively

**vitality** (32) energy

**vitiated** (77) undermined

**vitriolic** (6) nasty

**vivacious** (67, 95) lively and exciting

**vivacity** (17) liveliness

**vivified** (68) added liveliness to

**vociferated** (37) shouted

**void** (80) empty nothingness

**volatile** (36, 63) easily exploding / becoming violent

**volley** (36) outburst

**vowed** (63) promised

**vying** (78) competing

*Waialae* (28) wealthy suburb of Honolulu

**wallowing** (50) reveling

**wantonness** (58) irresponsibility

**wary** (89) cautiously watchful

**wayward** (58,63) stubborn and disobedient

**weather** (73) survive

**welling** (78) rising to the surface and ready to flow

**whetting** (59) stimulating

**whimpered** (48) sobbed softly or weakly

**whims** (48) sudden ideas or desires

**whisked** (25) rushed

*Whitney Houston* (9) 1980s singer

**wholesome** (30) healthy

**wielding** (14) carrying / exercising

**willful** (45, 55) intentional

**winsome** (29) charming

**withdrawn** (4) reclusively shy

**witless** (25) stupid

**wonderment** (28) astonishment and curiosity

**wondrous** (95) marvelous

**wretched** (49) miserable

**writhing** (59) twisting

**wrongheaded** (51) misguidedly stubborn

**yearn** (2, 23, 49) want

**zealous** (26) fanatic

**zephyr** (97) gentle breeze